SUPERMAN

THE DEATH OF SUPERMAN

SUPERMAN
THE DEATH OF SUPERMAN

writers DAN JURGENS JERRY ORDWAY LOUISE SIMONSON ROGER STERN

pencillers JON BOGDANOVE TOM GRUMMETT JACKSON GUICE DAN JURGENS

inkers BRETT BREEDING RICK BURCHETT DOUG HAZLEWOOD Dennis JANKE DENIS RODIER

colorists GENE D'ANGELO GLENN WHITMORE

letterers JOHN COSTANZA ALBERT DeGUZMAN BILL OAKLEY WILLIE SCHUBERT

collection cover artists DAN JURGENS, BRETT BREEDING and JOHN KALISZ

DOOMSDAY created by BRETT BREEDING, JERRY ORDWAY, LOUISE SIMONSON, ROGER STERN and DAN JURGENS.

Mike Carlin, Brian Augustyn Editors - Original Series **Jennifer Frank, Ruben Diaz** Assistant Editors - Original Series
Jeb Woodard Group Editor - Collected Editions **Steve Cook** Design Director - Books **Damian Ryland** Publication Design

Bob Harras Senior VP - Editor-in-Chief, DC Comics

Diane Nelson President	**Alison Gill** Senior VP - Manufacturing & Operations
Dan DiDio and **Jim Lee** Co-Publishers	**Hank Kanalz** Senior VP - Editorial Strategy & Administration
Geoff Johns Chief Creative Officer	**Jay Kogan** VP - Legal Affairs
Amit Desai Senior VP - Marketing & Global Franchise Management	**Derek Maddalena** Senior VP - Sales & Business Development
Nairi Gardiner Senior VP - Finance	**Jack Mahan** VP - Business Affairs
Sam Ades VP - Digital Marketing	**Dan Miron** VP - Sales Planning & Trade Development
Bobbie Chase VP - Talent Development	**Nick Napolitano** VP - Manufacturing Administration
Mark Chiarello Senior VP - Art, Design & Collected Editions	**Carol Roeder** VP - Marketing
John Cunningham VP - Content Strategy	**Eddie Scannell** VP - Mass Account & Digital Sales
Anne DePies VP - Strategy Planning & Reporting	**Courtney Simmons** Senior VP - Publicity & Communications
Don Falletti VP - Manufacturing Operations	**Jim (Ski) Sokolowski** VP - Comic Book Specialty & Newsstand Sales
Lawrence Ganem VP - Editorial Administration & Talent Relations	**Sandy Yi** Senior VP - Global Franchise Management

SUPERMAN: THE DEATH OF SUPERMAN WARNER HOME VIDEO EDITION

PEFC Certified
Printed on paper from
sustainably managed
forests and controlled
sources
PEFC/01-31-106   www.pefc.org

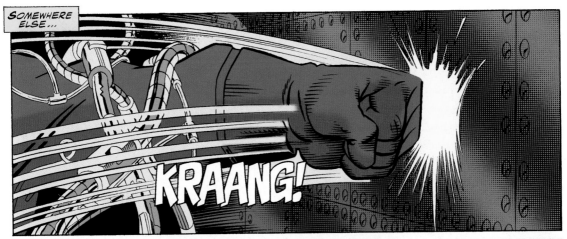

SOMEWHERE ELSE...

KRAANG!

KRAANG!

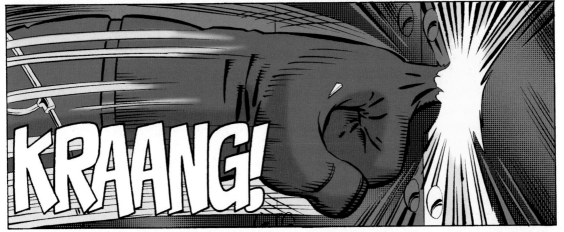

KRAANG!

KRAANG!

...DOOMSDAY IS COMING!

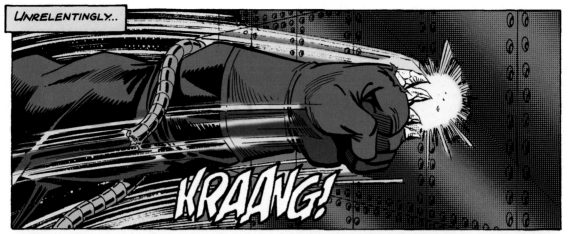

KRAANG!

KRAANG!

KRAANG!

KRIINK!

...DOOMSDAY IS COMING!

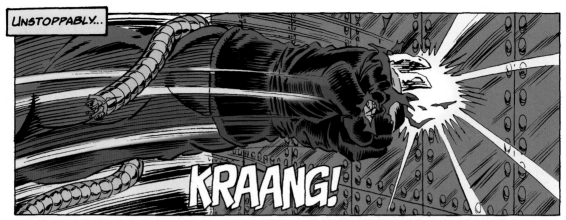

UNSTOPPABLY...

KRAANG!

KRAANG!

KRAANG!

KRAAK!

...DOOMSDAY IS COMING!

UNBELIEVABLY...

KRAANG!

KRAANG!

KRAANG!

KROOM!

...DOOMSDAY IS HERE!

HERE LIES
EARTH'S GREATEST
HERO

DOOMSDAY!

STORY : LOUISE SIMONSON

PENCILLER : JON BOGDANOVE

INKER : DENNIS JANKE

LETTERER : BILL OAKLEY

COLORIST : GLENN WHITMORE

"-- WHEN THE GUYS I'M GOIN' AFTER ARE *MONSTERS!*"

THIS *POWER STATION* IS *OURS!*

SO... HOW DO WE *GO* ABOUT DIVERTING THE POWER TO OUR *WAR MACHINES?*

I DO WHAT YOU *SAY*, CLAWSTER. FOR NOW, *YOU* THE *BOSS*.

KEEP ENGINEER *HYPNOTIZED*, KATHANA!

YOU *HEAR* CHARLIE, MAN! SO *TALK!* TELL US WHERE IS *SWITCH* SO WE CAN STEAL *ELECTRICITY!*

CURTIS

THE MAIN *CONTROL BOARD...* IS OVER *THERE!*

FOOD, JUICE, FLASHLIGHT, EXTRA BATTERIES, SPRAY PAINT...

CHILDREN'S COATES CH...

...DREN'S ...ID ...CIETY ...LDRENS CENTER

WHY IS IT I KEEP THINKIN' I'M DOIN' SOMETHING *DUMB?*

MAYBE I BETTER GO OVER MY *PLAN* ONE MORE TIME?

THE MONSTERS IN THE SEWERS SAY THEY GOT MY *MOMMA...*

...AN' THEY'LL *KILL* HER IF I TELL ANY-BODY THAT THEY WANNA MAKE WAR ON THE CITY!

BUT... WHAT IF THEY'RE *LYIN'?* WHAT IF THEY'RE TRYIN' TA *TRICK* ME?

WHAT IF THEY DON'T HAVE MY *MOMMA* AT ALL?

14

BUT--THEY CAN'T BE LYIN'-- CAN THEY?

MOMMA DIDN'T COME BACK TA GET ME FROM THE ORPHANAGE 'CAUSE SHE COULDN'T.

'CAUSE SHE'S THE MONSTERS' PRISONER.

SHE WANTS TO COME, BUT SHE CAN'T. BUT I'LL SAVE HER.

AN' SHE'LL HUG ME AN' TELL ME HOW BRAVE I AM AN' ASK ME TO STAY WITH HER ALWAYS...

...AN' I'LL BRING HER OUT AN' THEN I'LL TELL SUPERMAN 'BOUT THE MONSTERS' PLAN.

THERE'RE GONNA BE A LOT MORE FORKS IN THE TUNNELS DOWN HERE. I HOPE THIS WORKS.

PSSSR

AWRIIIGHT! MOMMA AN' ME CAN'T GET LOST NOW!

HI, LOIS! HOW'RE THE ARTICLES ON THE CONFISCATED ELECTRONICS THE COPS "LOST"?

WELL ENOUGH. MY SOURCE IN THE HARBOR PATROL TELLS ME-- WHAT'S THIS?

SEND SUPERMAN TO THE BASEMENT UNDER THE WEST SIDE POWER STATION. METROPOLIS IS IN DANGER!

- A FRIEND

CLARK ISN'T AROUND. DARN. SOMETIMES HE FORGETS TO CHECK HIS MAIL....

...ESPECIALLY WHEN HE HEADS DOWN FROM THE ROOF.

"ANONYMOUS TIP SAYS THERE'S DANGER IN THE BASEMENT OF THE WEST SIDE POWER STATION. MEET ME THERE! LOIS"

THAT SHOULD DO IT!

LOIS--?

GOTTA RUN, FRAN! WOULD YOU TELL CLARK THERE'S A MESSAGE FOR HIM ON HIS COMPUTER?

SCANNED THE CITY, BUT DIDN'T SEE ANY UNDER-WORLDERS ON THE SURFACE.

MUST BE LYING LOW FOR NOW, MAYBE IT'S TIME--

"--I GOT BACK TO WORK!"

HI, CLARK, LOIS LEFT YOU A COMPUTER MESSAGE.

VERY HIGH TECH OF HER. THANKS, FRAN.

TAK-TAP-TAK-TAP!

READ: MESSAGES

WHAT NOW?

ALL THE COMPUTERS DON'T WORK?

LIGHTS, EITHER!

DON'T TELL ME... WE'RE HAVING ANOTHER BLACKOUT?!

WE DO IT!

YEAAAA!

WE STEAL METROPOLIS'S ELECTRICITY!

NOW CITY IS HELPLESS... AND UNDERWORLD CAN KICK BUTT!

17

WHO *ARE* YOU? WHAT'S GOING ON? CHARLIE-- HOW COULD YOU?

IT EASY, REPORTER LADY. AN' *SMART.* YOU HELP TEACH CHARLIE, DIDN'T YOU?

HE SOCIETY'S REJECT... LIKE US ALL.

YOU WANT TO GIVE US *HANDOUTS!*

BUT *UNDER-WORLD* GOTS WAR MACHINES NOW... AN' WE TAKE WHAT WE WANT!

SHE MIGHT BE USEFUL AS A *HOSTAGE,* CLAW. BETTER BRING HER TO THE BOSS.

YOU *TEASE* HER, CHARLIE. YOU *KNOW* BOSS DON'T TAKE *PRISONERS!*

SHE BE *DEAD* 'FORE HOUR IS UP!

NO *PRISONERS?* BUT WHAT ABOUT MY *MOMMA?*

THEY... THEY NEVER *HAD* MY MOMMA! THEY *LIED* TO ME SO I WOULDN'T TALK!

I-I GUESS... I KNEW... ALL ALONG THEY DIDN'T HAVE HER. I JUST WANTED TO *BELIEVE...*

...THAT I COULD *FIND* HER... AN' *SAVE* HER...

...AN' *MAKE* HER *LOVE* ME.

ELSEWHERE...

KRAK
KRAM!

KRAKK!

20

THE MONSTERS DON'T HAVE MY MOMMA.

THIS PROBABLY MEANS I'M NEVER GONNA FIND HER...

BUT THEY REALLY DO HAVE THAT REPORTER LADY.

THEY'RE GONNA KILL HER. AN' ATTACK THE CITY.

THAT'S REAL. I CAN STOP THAT. AN' THAT MEANS TELLIN' SUPERMAN--FAST!

IT'S AWFUL DARK UP HERE! WHERE ARE THE STREET LIGHTS?

I BET THE MONSTERS DID IT.

I READ HOW THEY USE A BAT SYMBOL TO CALL BATMAN. ONLY IT'S IN THE SKY...

FFSSSTT

...AN' THIS ONE'S ON THE GROUND.

FPSSSSSTT

IT'S ALL MY FAULT! IF I TOLD SUPERMAN, 'STEAD OF BELIEVIN' MONSTERS' LIES...

...HE WOULDA ALREADY STOPPED 'EM!

I JUST HOPE MY IDEA WORKS!

SUPERMAN! SUPERMAN! PLEASE PLEASE SEE THE SIGNAL!

KEITH?

SUPERMAN, IT'S YOU! I KNEW YOU'D COME!

THERE'S THIS REPORTER LADY IN THE TUNNELS! MONSTERS HAVE HER--

"--AN' THEY'RE GONNA INVADE THE CITY!"

SOON... SOON OUR *BORER* WILL CARVE A SUBTERRANEAN *HIGHWAY* THROUGH THE BEDROCK!

THEN OUR *WAR MACHINES* ROLL UP THROUGH TUNNEL...

...AN' *METROPOLIS* WILL BE IN HANDS OF MONSTERS!

SKREEDH!

THE BORER! IT'S STOPPED! BUT WHY?!

TK-TK! (IT SHOVING BACK AT US OUT OF HOLE!) TK-TK!

HUrf! IT... ...SUPERMAN! HUrf!

SUPERMAN?! RAMBEAU-- DIVERSION 7!

I...UH...GOT THE GRENADE, CLAWSTER, BUT WHERE DO I PUT IT?

IDIOT! HE GOT THE GRENADE!

WHAT DOES SUPERMAN CARE WHAT'S DESTROYED IN THIS-- HEY!

I'VE ABOUT HAD IT WITH YOUR DISTRACTIONS, CLAWSTER!

SO EAT "DIVERSION 7"!

?!

BWAAMF!

GOOD THING CLAWSTER...

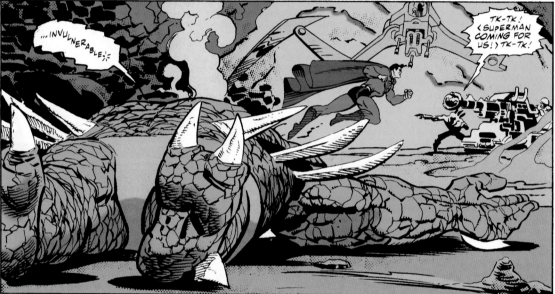

...INVULNERABLE!

TK-TK! ‹SUPERMAN COMING FOR US!› TK-TK!

TK-TK! ‹ACTIVATE WAR MACHINES! NOW!› TK-TK!

SHRAKT!

THE *JAILS* ON THE SURFACE WON'T *HOLD* THESE GUYS!

WE'LL HOLD A *TRIAL* AND DEAL WITH THEM IN *UNDERWORLD.*

BUT... YOU DON'T HAVE TO *STAY* DOWN HERE, YOU KNOW.

THERE'S A *PLACE* FOR YOU AND YOUR FRIENDS IN *METROPOLIS.*

YOU *KIDDIN',* RIGHT?

AIN'T NUTHIN' FOR *US* ON THE SURFACE, AN' *CHARLIE* AN' ME'RE HUMAN.

AN' IT'S NOT LIKE MY FRIENDS GOT *MARKETABLE* SKILLS OR NUTHIN'. NAH...

...WE JAWED 'BOUT IT BEFORE, AN' WE DECIDED TA STAY IN THE *TUNNELS.*

WHAT ABOUT *YOU,* CHARLIE?

I COULD TRY TO GET YOU A JOB AT THE *PLANET.* YOU'RE PRETTY GOOD AT FERRETING OUT INFORMATION.

THANKS, MISS LANE. BUT I'LL TAKE MY CHANCES HERE.

THEN... MAYBE YOU CAN BE OUR *UNDERWORLD CORRESPONDENT?*

DEAL!

YA KNOW, GRUB, THERE'S WORSE DOWN HERE THAN THE *WAR-WORLDERS.*

YOU THINK I SHOULD *TELL* 'EM... MY DUTY AS A *CORRESPONDENT* AN' ALL?

NAH, BLOODTHIRST IS *OUR* PROBLEM. BUT IT'S GOOD TO KNOW IF WE CAN'T HANDLE 'IM...

...WE CAN CALL IN *SUPERMAN!*

31

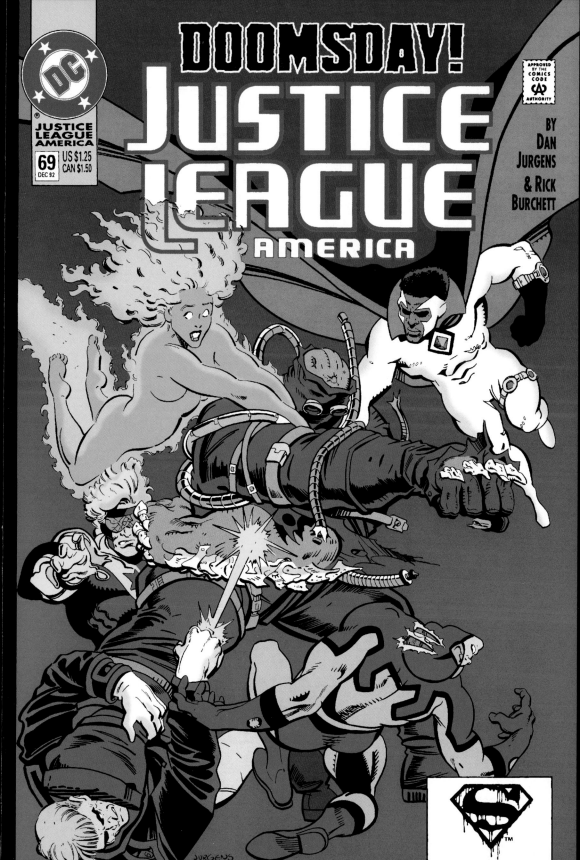

Here Lies Earth's Greatest Hero

MY ICE WILL MELT SOME OF THE BLAZE!

GOOD MOVE, *ICE!* THE REST OF US WILL TAKE CARE OF THE VICTIMS!

TSSSSSSS

WE SURE APPRECIATE THE HELP, JUSTICE LEAGUERS! I'M WELL AWARE THAT *OHIO* IS OUT OF YOUR NORMAL AREA OF JURISDICTION--

WE MUST FIND THE BEAST.

I AGREE, BLOODWYND. EVERYBODY INTO THE BUG AND WE'LL BE ON OUR WAY.

GOSH, IT'S TOO BAD WE HAVE THIS EMERGENCY! I REALLY WANTED TO SEE TODAY'S EPISODE--

"--OF THE *CAT GRANT* SHOW."

WE'RE COMING TO YOU *LIVE* FROM ROOSEVELT HIGH WITH AN *INCREDIBLE* SHOW!

HE IS PERHAPS THE MOST CELEBRATED MAN OF OUR TIME! HE'S BEEN CALLED THE MAN OF TOMORROW--

--THE LAST SON OF KRYPTON AND THE MAN OF STEEL! BUT HE'S MOST APPROPRIATELY KNOWN AS--

"--SUPERMAN!"

YEAH!

YAYYY

CLAP CLAP

CLAP CLAP CLAP

KEEP YOUR EYES ON THE GROUND, PEOPLE! THE SOONER WE SPOT OUR MONSTER THE BETTER!

HEY, BEETLE, IF IT'S A REALLY COOL MONSTER MAYBE WE SHOULD CAPTURE IT--

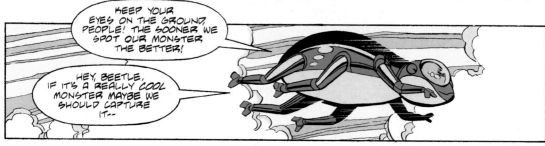

--AND TAKE IT ON THE TALK-SHOW CIRCUIT FOR BIG BUCKS!

YOUR SENSE OF THE APPROPRIATE KNOWS NO LIMITS, BOOSTER.

IT TOOK YOU THIS LONG TO REALIZE THAT, BLOODWYND?

Uh-oh...LOOKS LIKE WE'VE FOUND OUR MAN'S TRAIL OF CRUMBS!

CHECK OUT THAT PATH OF DESTRUCTION!

THOSE TREES WEREN'T MOWED DOWN BY A COUPLE OF KIDS ON SKATE-BOARDS!

THIS IS TERRIBLE! SUCH POINT-LESS...NEEDLESS DEVASTATION!

LET'S JUST FIND THE SUCKERS AND KICK SOME BUTT!

I CAN'T THANK YOU ENOUGH FOR JOINING US HERE, SUPERMAN. INTERVIEWS WITH YOU ARE A TRUE RARITY!

I'VE ALWAYS FELT THAT IF AMERICANS ARE TO *TRUST* US, THEY HAVE TO *KNOW* US, MS. GRANT.

AND WITHOUT YOUR TRUST WE ARE *NOT* EFFECTIVE.

YOU'VE EXHIBITED *PSYCHIC POWERS* BEFORE, *BLOODWYND*. ANY CHANCE YOU CAN SCAN AHEAD AND TAP INTO THIS GUY'S MIND?

IT WILL BE *DIFFICULT*--

--BUT I CAN TRY.

AS WILL I--

I GUESS *TWO PSYCHIC MINDS* ARE *BETTER* THAN ONE.

NUTS! I WANTED BLOODWYND TO GO IT ALONE SO I'D HAVE A CHANCE TO GAUGE HIS POWERS!

IT'S THE ONLY WAY I CAN GET *INFO* ON THE GUY!

THE WAY HE SHIELDS HIS ABILITIES HE'LL PROBABLY *LET* MAXIMA MAKE FIRST CONTACT EVEN IF--

YES!

I'VE FOUND THE CREATURE!

HE'S *HATE*--

--*DEATH* AND *BLOOD LUST* PERSONIFIED!

NOTHING *MORE.*

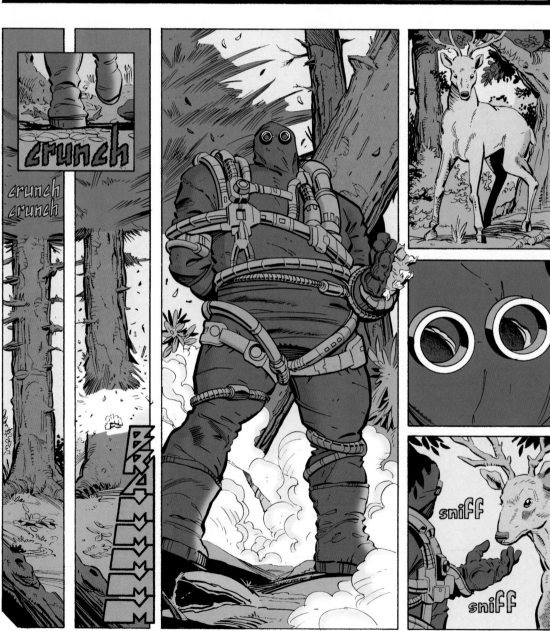

IT'S UNFAIR TO THE OTHERS TO PAINT ME AS THE *LEADER* OF THE JUSTICE LEAGUE.

WE'RE A GROUP OF PEOPLE WHO HAVE GOTTEN TOGETHER TO DO A JOB ONLY WE CAN DO.

EVERYBODY IN THE GROUP HAS A SAY ON ISSUES... AND A VOTE AS WELL.

GLURTCH

CRACKK

HA HA HAA!

?

SHRAK

THIS INTERVIEW IS TAKING PLACE IN METROPOLIS FOR THE BENEFIT OF HIGH SCHOOLS NATIONWIDE. I WANT YOU KIDS TO PAY *ATTENTION!*

IF YOU ASK ME, IT'S A *YAWNER,* MITCH.

NO *KIDDIN'!* THEY *SHOULDA* TALKED TO *GUY GARDNER--*

Next Assignment chapter!

"--IF THEY WANTED TO TALK TO SOMEONE WITH THEIR HEAD *SCREWED* ON STRAIGHT!"

HA HA HAA!

LET GO OF HIM, YOU *MONSTER!*

EEF!

THAT *FREAKIN'* THING'S *POWERFUL!* NEVER HAD A CHANCE TO FIGHT *BACK!*

CAN'T BREATHE...

CAN'T... ...EVEN... ...THINK...

48

GOOD QUESTION, MISS. SEE, ONE WAY OR ANOTHER, FEAR IS ALWAYS PART OF THE JOB.

I'M AFRAID OF FAILURE AND AFRAID OF HURTING INNOCENT PEOPLE AND, TO BE CANDID--

--I'VE BEEN AFRAID FOR MYSELF. I HAVE ENCOUNTERED THINGS POWERFUL ENOUGH TO KILL ME.

HEH!

HA!

OH!

YOU GUYS TAKE CARE OF THE STEROID CASE! I'LL GET BLOODWYND OUT OF THAT INFERNO!

WEIRD! HERE I AM TRYING TO SAVE THE MOST MYSTERIOUS GUY IN THE LEAGUE! BLOODWYND IS HIDING SOMETHING FROM US THAT--

THERE! BUT THAT'S NOT--

OF COURSE! ALL THIS TIME I'VE WONDERED WHO BLOODWYND REALLY IS AND NOW I KNOW! I NEVER WOULD HAVE GUESSED IT IN A MILLION YEARS--

--BUT BLOODWYND IS REALLY--

WHAT ABOUT ALL THAT, Y'KNOW, HITTING AND VIOLENCE? DON'T YOU GET TIRED OF IT?

I MEAN, ISN'T THERE A BETTER WAY TO WORK THINGS OUT THAN CAVING IN SOMEONE'S HEAD?

HEH!!

BLOODWYND MUST BE-- AWK!

AH

Nnng...

KANG

CRACK

FWOOM

HA HA!

...SOMEONE...

...HELLLP...

...MEEE...

BELIEVE ME WHEN I SAY I WISH THAT VIOLENCE *WASN'T* NECESSARY.

BUT VIOLENCE IS THE PRICE WE PAY TO ACCOMPLISH A GREATER GOOD.

AS HEROES, WE CHOOSE TO PROTECT THAT GOOD--

"--WITH OUR LIVES."

HA!

BEETLE WILL NEVER SURVIVE IF I DO NOT--

BOOM

LOOK OU--

AHH!

CUT! WE'VE JUST BEEN PREEMPTED BY A NETWORK *SPECIAL REPORT!*

SOUNDS LIKE TROUBLE IN OHIO.

WONDER IF IT'S ANYTHING I CAN HELP WITH.

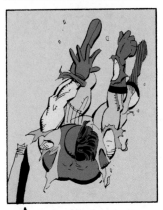

WHUMP

TED! OH, NO! HE'S SO STILL....

SO QUIET...

OH MY GOD! WE NEED TO GET HIM TO A HOSPITAL, QUICK!

I THINK IT MAY BE TOO LATE, BOOSTER!

BUT I PRAY I'M WRONG.

NOOOO!

53

--HAVE REPORTS OF THE JUSTICE LEAGUE BATTLING A HEINOUS MONSTER AT A LEXOIL REFINERY IN OHIO. REPORTS INDICATE THE LEAGUE IS UNABLE TO STOP HIS DESTRUCTIVE STAMPEDE.

SUPERMAN...

I HAVE TO GO.

I'M TIRED OF PLAYING TAG WITH YOU, UGLY!

LET'S SEE, YOU WALK AWAY FROM A FULL-INTENSITY BLAST!

BAH!

HE'S STILL COMING! GOTTA GET MY FORCE FIELD UP BEFORE--

HA HA HAA!

AAAUHH!

HOW COULD ONE MAN STAND AGAINST THE WHOLE LEAGUE?

SOON AS I'M UP OVER THE HORIZON, I'LL BE ABLE TO CHECK THINGS OUT WITH MY TELESCOPIC VISION!

MAN, I JUST *BARELY* RAISED MY FORCE FIELD IN TIME.

THE FORCE OF HIS BLOW IS OVERPOWERING MY FLIGHT RING. IF HE CAN DO THIS TO ME--

--IMAGINE WHAT HE DID TO BEETLE.

WONDER IF THAT RUBBER-SUITED POWERHOUSE IS BIOLOGICAL--

--OR SOME KIND OF *DOOMSDAY* MACHINE!

THAT'S FAR ENOUGH, BOOSTER.

YOU!

56

Here Lies Earth's Greatest Hero

THEN OUR COMRADE SHALL PERISH AS A WARRIOR FALLEN IN BATTLE.

THERE IS NO GREATER HONOR ONE CAN ATTAIN.

NO, *MAXIMA!* YOU CAN'T JUST LEAVE HIM HERE TO *DIE!*

WE HAVE TO GET HIM TO A DOCTOR BEFORE IT'S TOO *LATE!*

I DON'T HAVE THE POWER TO DO THAT BUT *YOU* DO! YOU HAVE TO GIVE HIM A CHANCE AT *LIFE!*

NO.

THERE IS A BATTLE TO BE FOUGHT HERE.

A DESTRUCTIVE CREATURE IS ON A RAMPAGE THAT COULD KILL HUNDREDS.

PERHAPS ONLY AN ALMERACIAN MAY HAVE THE POWER TO STOP HIM.

PLEASE, MAXIMA, YOU'RE PART OF A TEAM... PART OF A *FAMILY* NOW!

LOOK AROUND YOU!

THIS CREEP IS TOUGH... THAT MUCH IS OBVIOUS.

BUT RIGHT NOW ONLY *YOU* CAN SAVE TED KORD'S LIFE.

LET ME GO AFTER THE MONSTER UNTIL YOU GET BACK.

I AM A WARRIOR. IT IS AGAINST MY NATURE TO LET OTHERS DO MY WORK.

YET YOU AIDED ME IN MY STRUGGLES AGAINST STARBREAKER.

I OWE YOU *MY* AID IN RETURN.

I HOPE YOU CAN SURVIVE THE MONSTER'S WRATH UNTIL MY RETURN.

FOR NOW... BLUE BEETLE SHALL RECEIVE HIS MEDICAL CARE.

THANK YOU, MAXIMA.

BUT NOW COMES THE HARD PART!

SOMEHOW I'VE GOT TO STOP THIS MANIAC BY MYSELF--

--EVEN THOUGH HE'S ALREADY SHREDDED THE WHOLE *TEAM!*

BUT IF I USE MY BRAINS AND KEEP MY DISTANCE I MIGHT BE ABLE TO HOLD HIM OFF UNTIL MAXIMA GETS BACK.

BOOSTER MIGHT EVEN STILL BE A HELP--

--BUT I DOUBT IT! THAT HORROR HAS PROBABLY PUT HIM IN ORBIT BY NOW!

WEIRD! IT'S TOTALLY UNYIELDING!

HE JUST MARCHES STRAIGHT AHEAD WITHOUT DEVIATING FROM HIS COURSE--NO MATTER WHAT HE FINDS IN HIS PATH!

AND IF MEMORY SERVES--

"--THERE'S A HOUSING DEVELOPMENT RIGHT OVER THAT HILL!"

MAN, DO I LOVE FRIDAYS.

NO MORE SUCKY SCHOOL FOR TWO WHOLE DAYS!

TOO BAD I GOTTA GO HOME TO THE WAR ZONE.

I CAN JUST HEAR MOM NOW. *"MITCH, DEAR, IS THAT YOU? HOW WAS YOUR DAY?"*

WHY DOES SHE ALWAYS HAVE TO BE SO CORNY?

WHAT DID SHE DO TO MAKE DAD *LEAVE* US?

HOME SWEET HOME.

WHAT A DUMP, I MEAN, I *HATE* THIS HOLE.

MITCH, DEAR, IS THAT YOU?

NO, IT'S AXL ROSE AND THE BAND.

WE GOT ANYTHING WORTH EATING AROUND HERE?

HELP YOURSELF TO THE FRIDGE. HOW WAS SCHOOL? DID YOU DO WELL ON YOUR ALGEBRA TEST?

LIKE YOU CARE.

HEY! WHAT HAPPENED TO ALL THE SODA?

OF *COURSE* I CARE. SAY, WASN'T TODAY THE DAY THAT SUPERMAN WAS GOING TO ADDRESS HIGH SCHOOL STUDENTS ON TV?

YOU MUST HAVE BEEN *THRILLED* TO SEE THAT!

NO WAY. THE SUPER WEASEL WAS CALLED AWAY ON SOME CASE SO HE BAILED EARLY.

WHY DO WE ALWAYS RUN OUT OF SODA AROUND HERE? WHY CAN'T YOU EVER *BUY* ENOUGH TO LAST?

LOOK, I'M SORRY, BUT YOUR LITTLE SISTER ISN'T FEELING WELL SO I DIDN'T HAVE TIME TO GO SHOPPING TODAY!

I AM REALLY TIRED OF THAT *BABY* BEING THE ONLY ONE WHO RATES AROUND HERE!

I MEAN, DAD *ALWAYS* HAS SODA FOR ME AT HIS NEW APARTMENT!

I AM SORRY, MITCHELL, BUT I CANNOT KEEP *UP* WITH EVERYTHING HERE!

THIS HOUSE ISN'T PERFECT AND NEITHER AM I BUT WE DO THE BEST WE CAN!

JEEZ.

NO WONDER DAD LEFT AND WANTS A DIVORCE.

GOIN' OVER TO AARON'S.

SEE YOU.

COOO! COOO!

WAIT! DID YOU HEAR THAT--

SKRASSH WHUMP

BECKY...! THE GLASS!

OH, MAN!

MITCHELL, I WANT YOU TO CALL 911! HURRY!

OH, GOD... OUTSIDE IN THE DRIVE-WAY...

OUR CAR!

CHECK IT OUT!

THAT DUDE DID ALL THIS-- WITH ONE HAND TIED BEHIND HIS BACK!?

RRRR RAAGH!

:OOOOF!:

GET DOWN!

CRASH!

KTTTSH

SKKASSH!

UNBELIEVABLE!

BUDDADOOM

BKOW!

I DON'T KNOW IF I'VE EVER BEEN HIT THAT HARD!

AMAZING! I CAN'T EVEN SEE HIM ANYMORE BUT I THINK HE'S STILL STANDING!

DON'T STAND THERE BLABBIN', BLUE! JUST TURN UP THE JUICE!

GETTING TIRED...

IGNORE IT, FIRE! JUST KEEP PUSHIN'!

NO! MY FLAME IS TOTALLY SPENT!

CAN'T GO... ANYMORE!

SAME HERE!

MY POWER CELLS ARE SHOT --DRAINED!

AND WITHOUT MY SUIT'S POWERS I'M ABOUT AS POWERFUL AS PEE WEE HERMAN!

OKAY, LET'S GIVE IT A REST! AFTER ALL THIS--

-- THERE'S NO WAY DOOMSDAY CAN STILL BE STANDIN'!

WITH... POWER CELLS GONE I'M IN *DEEP* TROUBLE!

FORCE FIELD-- GONE!

RRAH!

HA!

HE'S... FASTER THAN... FLASH! CAN'T GET...

SHRIIPP

RRRR

NO!

HA!

SLAMM

WHAT IS THAT-- *THING?*

CAN'T FIGHT... BUT I CAN AT LEAST *HELP* YOU!

BUT WHAT ABOUT-- *THAT?* WHAT *IS* IT?

MAYBE A ROBOT... OR *SOMETHING* FROM ANOTHER DIMENSION! WHATEVER--

"--IT'S DEADLY!"

CAN'T SEE, BUT I CAN HEAR THE BONES BREAKIN'!

GOTTA POINT... BLAST... AND HOPE!

HFFF?

HA!

UHN!

I SHALL BLAST THIS HORROR--

TWO-FRONT OFFENSIVE NOW!

¡UGH!

EERK!

MY EYE BEAMS!

NOOOOO!

JEEZ! BAD ENOUGH THE MONSTER IS TRASHING US! THE LEAGUE DOESN'T HAVE TO HELP!

OH, GOD... IF THAT BLAZE HAS GOTTEN TO ONE OF THE GAS LINES IN THE HOUSE...

BWHOOOOOM!

CRIPES!

TORA? TORA? ARRRR!

THUD

WHERE... WHERE IS EVERYBODY?

MA? ARE YOU OKAY?

MA?!

SO--- *KAFF* MUCH SMOKE...

CAN'T... BREATHE, CAN'T...

HAHAHA

NO.

NO WAY--

--IS THAT MANIAC ESCAPING ME!

MA!

OH, MAN, SHE MUST BE HURT OR SOMETHING!

THE FIRE'S SURROUNDED US! I'LL NEVER GET HER OUT OF HERE!

NEED HELP...BUT THE JLA LOOKS WAY OUT OF IT OR WORSE!

"FIRE--

"ICE--

"--BOOSTER GOLD...THE BLOOD GUY--

"--EVEN GUY GARDNER!"

THE ONLY ONE WHO CAN HELP US--

--HAS ALREADY BUGGED OUT AFTER THAT KILLING MACHINE!

SUPERMAN!

78

I DON'T KNOW WHO OR WHAT EXACTLY THIS DOOMSDAY THING IS, BUT I'LL BEAT THE ANSWER OUT OF HIM IF I HAVE TO!

HE DOESN'T APPEAR TO HAVE ANY MAGICAL POWERS SO I WON'T HAVE TO WORRY ABOUT THAT!

PLEASE, SUPERMAN! YOU JUST GOTTA HEAR ME!

THAT BOY I SAW! I CAN HEAR HIM CALLING... BUT I HAVE TO IGNORE IT! I'M SO CLOSE!

HELP US! PLEASE!

IF I LET DOOMSDAY GET AWAY THERE'S NO TELLING WHAT DEVASTATION HE'LL BE RESPONSIBLE FOR.

MUCH AS IT PAINS ME-- I HAVE TO STAY WITH HIM AND BLOCK OUT THAT PLEA FOR HELP!

PLEASE, SUPERMAN...

...YOU JUST GOTTA COME BACK

PLEASE!

"THIS IS TOTALLY NUTS-- I COME HOME FROM SCHOOL, GET INTO ANOTHER FIGHT WITH MA..."

"...AND THEN ALL AT ONCE, THE FREAKIN'JUSTICE LEAGUE CRASHES DOWN ON US, ALONG WITH SOMEONE CALLED DOOMSDAY!"

"THE HOUSE IS A DISASTER AREA-- FLAMES ARE EVERYWHERE.

"THAT DOOMSDAY GUY DID IT ALL-- AND JUST BOOKED OUT OF HERE, WITH SUPERMAN ON HIS TAIL!"

"CAN'T HARDLY BELIEVE GUY GARDNER GOT SO BUSTED UP!"

"THOSE TWO BABES, ICE AND FIRE, MIGHT BE DEAD-- I CAN'T TELL FROM HERE..."

"...BUT FROM THE SOUND OF THINGS ABOUT TWENTY FEET AWAY, WHERE OUR FAMILY ROOM USED TO BE...

"...THAT BOOSTER GOLD MUST WISH HE WAS CROAKED!"

"I CAN HEAR MY MA, CALLING OUT TO ME, AND I ANSWER HER, BUT I CAN'T HELP HER OR MY BABY SISTER!"

"THROUGH THE THICK BLACK SMOKE, I SEE SUPERMAN, UP IN THE SKY--I HEAR THE SOUND OF HIS FISTS ALL OVER DOOMSDAY!"

"PLEASE, GOD--LET HIM HEAR MY CRIES FOR HELP!'"

UNDER FIRE

"NO ONE ELSE CAN HELP-- THE SIRENS ARE TOO FAR OFF--THEY'LL NEVER REACH US IN TIME.

"IT SEEMS LIKE THIS WHOLE DEAL HAS BEEN GOING ON FOR HOURS,'THOUGH IT'S PROBABLY ONLY BEEN MINUTES!'"

KAFF KAFF! MITCH, IT'S NO USE--I'VE GOT TO DO SOMETHING...!

TOM GRUMMETT - PENCILLER
DOUG HAZLEWOOD - INKER
JERRY ORDWAY - WRITER
ALBERT DE GUZMAN - LETTERER
GLENN WHITMORE - COLORIST

"SMOKE'S TOO THICK--MA'S GOT TO HOLD TIGHT! I'VE GOT TO YELL LOUDER--HE'S GOT TO HEAR ME!"

SUPERMAN! PLEASE-- YOU'VE GOT TO HELP US! MY MA'S TRAPPED-- PLEASE!

SUPERMAN-- YOU'RE THE ONLY ONE--HELP US!

¿KAFF¿ CAN'T GIVE UP--¿UGHNN¿ THAT KID AND HIS MOM DIDN'T ASK FOR--¿¿

¿KAFF·KAFF¿! GUY--IT HURTS-- MY RIBS--I CAN'T STAND UP TOO-- UHHN.

FOR GUY'S SAKE, I'VE GOT TO GET HIM UP--THAT MONSTER'S ALREADY PUT BLUE BEETLE INTO A COMA.

MY VOICE'S GOING--FROM BREATHIN' THIS SMOKE-- BUT I'VE GOTTA KEEP YELLIN'! UNLESS HE'S NOT LISTENING?

NAH, HE'S A HERO-- THEY'RE SUPPOSED TO HELP US! MAYBE THAT DOOMSDAY'S BEATING SUPERMAN? WHAT DO I DO THEN?

HELP US, SUPERMAN-- PLEASE!

I'VE GOT TO FORCE THIS THING FAR ENOUGH INTO THE LAKE'S SILT...

CHOOM

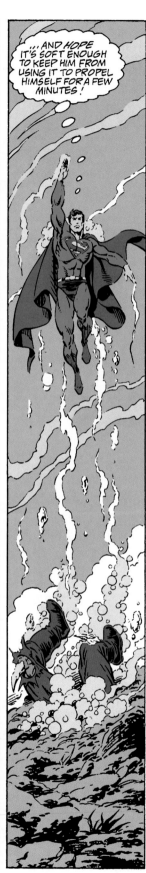

"...AND *HOPE* IT'S *SOFT* ENOUGH TO KEEP HIM FROM USING IT TO PROPEL HIMSELF FOR A FEW MINUTES!"

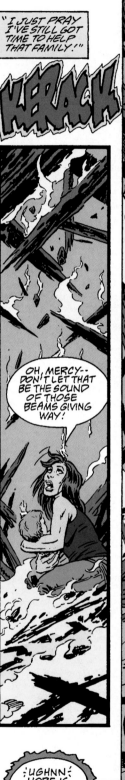

"I JUST PRAY I'VE STILL GOT TIME TO HELP THAT FAMILY!"

K'RACK

OH, MERCY-- DON'T LET THAT BE THE SOUND OF THOSE BEAMS GIVING WAY!

UGHNN! HOPE IS *NOT* LOST...

...NOT WHILE *BLOODWYND* STILL STANDS!

I DON'T KNOW *WHERE* YOU CAME FROM, MISTER-- BUT *THANK GOD* YOU'RE HERE!

YOU AND YOUR CHILD SHOULD ALSO THANK *SUPERMAN.*

BLOODWYND-- ARE YOU OKAY? YOU TOOK QUITE A BEATING--

ALL OF THE LEAGUERS *DID*-- BUT THIS GUY KEEPS SURPRISING ME WITH HIS--*RESILIENCY.*

S-SUPERMAN-- WHAT ABOUT MY *SON,* MITCH?

HE'S DOWN THERE WITH THE *E.M.S.* CREW, MISS.

THEY *DID* IT! THEY SAVED MY MOM AND MY BABY SISTER!

YOU SHOULD GO TO THE HOSPITAL-- YOU ALL TOOK IN A LOT OF SMOKE.

GUY-- LIE *STILL.*

HOW 'BOUT IT, FELLA? LET'S HAVE A LOOK AT YOU.

NO. I DESIRE *NO* MEDICAL TREATMENT.

I WISH TO BE *ALONE.*

ODD-- BLOODWYND'S TELEPORTED RATHER THAN SEEK TREATMENT--!

DON'T STRUGGLE-- WHAT *IS* IT?

KAFF KAFF! DON'T WUSS OUT, BOYSCOUT! PUT THIS DOOMSDAY GUY IN A *PINE BOX*--

--OR I'LL CRAWL OFFA THIS GURNEY AND *KICK BOTH O' YER BUTTS!* -- *KAFF*

I'LL TAKE CARE OF THINGS, GUY-- YOU JUST LET THE DOCTORS HELP YOU!

YOU THERE-- HAVE YOUR LOCAL HOSPITAL CONTACT MAXWELL LORD IN NEW YORK CITY FOR THESE FOLKS' MEDICAL RECORDS!

NOW TO SEE IF THIS "DOOMSDAY" IS STILL WHERE I LEFT HIM!

"QUESTION IS-- HOW DO I *RESTRAIN* HIM WHEN THE COMBINED FORCE OF THE *JUSTICE LEAGUE* COULDN'T DO IT?"

HOLY--! THAT'S OUR TARGET DOWN THERE, RALPH!

IT'S COMING UP FAST, BUT OUR WEAPONS SYSTEM'S LOCKED ON! COMMENCING LAUNCH OF HELL FIRES--

SPLASH!

88

SOMETHING TORE UP A STRETCH OF PROPERTY OUT ON ROUTE 110, RUSTY!

KIRBY COUNTY POLICE

LOWELL SAID A BUNCH OF FOLK--INCLUDING SOME OF THE *JUSTICE LEAGUE*--ARE BEING RUSHED TO THE HOSPITAL!

SAY, YOU *HEAR* THAT? KIND OF A *CARTOON* SOUND A *BOMB* MAKES JUST BEFORE IT--

SHOULD I CRANK UP THE *CIVIL DEFENSE* SIREN, CHIEF? MAYBE WE SHOULD GET EVERYONE INTO THEIR BASEMENTS--

MOTHER OF *PEARL!*

CRASH!

UH, CHIEF-- THINK I'M *GONNA* NEED A *BIGGER* GUN!

KIRBY COUNTY POLICE STATION

SAY... THERE'S THAT SOUND AGA--

THE GLOVES ARE OFF, DOOMSDAY! I'M TIRED OF TREADING LIGHTLY!

WHAMMMACK!

KA-DOOM!

HOT DAMN! THOSE GOOD OLD BOYS ARE TEARING UP MAIN STREET!

GET THE GOVERNOR ON THE PHONE!

:UGNHH:

IS--IT POSSIBLE THAT THIS GUY'S GETTING STRONGER?

WHO? WHO'S THAT?

RELAX, SOLDIER. YOU AND YOUR CO-PILOT ARE GOING TO BE OKAY...

...THOUGH I DON'T THINK THIS TOWN'S CITY HALL WILL BE OPEN FOR BUSINESS ANY TIME SOON!

"NOW EXCUSE ME, GUYS, BUT THERE ARE A DOZEN PEOPLE TRAPPED IN THAT WRECKAGE WHO NEED MY HELP!"

"STAND THERE AMID THE DESTRUCTION AND REVEL IN IT, WARRIOR!"

YOUR MOTIVES ARE UNCLEAR AS YET...

...BUT IF IT IS BATTLE YOU CRAVE, I, MAXIMA, AM PLEASED TO OBLIGE!

KA-POW

"YOU CAN'T JUST BARGE IN LIKE THAT, LADY!"

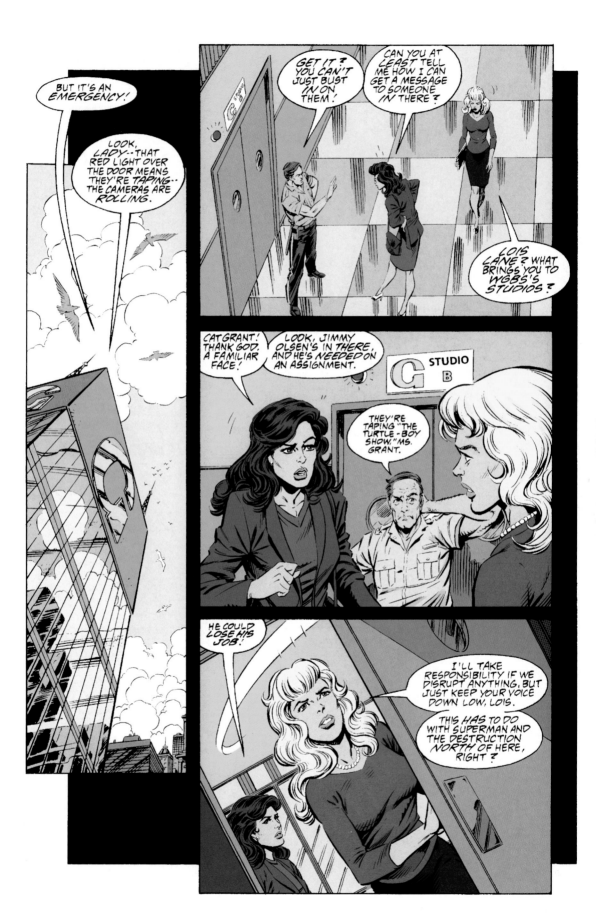

BUT IT'S AN EMERGENCY!

LOOK, LADY--THAT RED LIGHT OVER THE DOOR MEANS THEY'RE *TAPING*-- THE CAMERAS ARE *ROLLING*.

GET IT? YOU *CAN'T* JUST BUST IN ON THEM!

CAN YOU AT *LEAST* TELL ME HOW I CAN GET A MESSAGE TO SOMEONE IN THERE?

LOIS LANE? WHAT BRINGS YOU TO WGBS'S *STUDIOS?*

CAT GRANT! THANK GOD. A FAMILIAR FACE!

LOOK, JIMMY OLSEN'S IN *THERE*, AND HE'S NEEDED ON AN ASSIGNMENT.

THEY'RE TAPING "THE TURTLE-BOY SHOW," MS. GRANT.

G STUDIO B

HE COULD LOSE HIS JOB!

I'LL TAKE RESPONSIBILITY IF WE DISRUPT ANYTHING, BUT JUST KEEP YOUR VOICE DOWN LOW, LOIS.

THIS *HAS* TO DO WITH SUPERMAN AND THE DESTRUCTION *NORTH* OF HERE, RIGHT?

HI, "TURTLE-BOX."

WHAT'S GOING ON?

JIMMY-- THE CHIEF WILL HAVE YOUR HIDE! YOUR LUNCH HOUR ISN'T THREE HOURS LONG!

LOIS!

ERR, TAPING RAN A LITTLE LONG, BUT THIS IS MY FIRST TV SHOW.

WHY ARE YOU WHISPERING?

PERRY WANTS US TO COVER THIS "DOOMSDAY" INCIDENT. NED'S WAITING FOR US AT THE HELI-PAD! HURRY UP!

YOU TWO BETTER LOOK AT SOMETHING FIRST, GBS IS ABOUT TO INTERRUPT "THE BRAVE AND THE BOLD" FOR A NEWSBREAK.

COME ON, "TURTLE-BOY!"

THAT'S MISTER "TURTLE-BOY" TO YOU.

SURE, FINE. JUST LEAVE BEFORE WE'RE FINISHED, WHY DON'T YOU?

HI, LEON. MIND IF WE WATCH?

NOPE.

THIS IS A GBS NEWSBREAK. I'M STEVE LOMBARD.

THE DESTRUCTIVE FORCE KNOWN AS "DOOMSDAY" HAS LEFT THIRTY DEAD IN ITS WAKE...

...HUNDREDS HAVE BEEN INJURED, INCLUDING MEMBERS OF THE FAMED JUSTICE LEAGUE.

DOOMSDAY

IT APPEARS "DOOMSDAY" IS ON A STRAIGHT PATH CROSSING FROM OHIO THROUGH NEW YORK STATE...

"...SOME THEORIZE THAT THE CREATURE IS ON A COURSE STRAIGHT TO--OR THROUGH--METROPOLIS."

WE NOW RETURN YOU TO "THE BRAVE AND THE BOLD," ALREADY IN PROGRESS.

BLOODY--!

LEX, I SHOULD GO-- MAYBE I CAN LEND A HAND.

THERE'S GOT TO BE A MILLION THINGS I COULD--

LISTEN, COVE--YOU CAN'T JUST *UP* AND RUN OFF LIKE YOU DID DURING THAT SATANUS BUSINESS.

I NEED MY SUPERGIRL HERE WITH ME...

"...WE NEED A CONTINGENCY PLAN IN CASE THIS MENACE MAKES HIS WAY TO METROPOLIS."

BY THE HOUSE OF ALMERAC--YOU STILL STAND, EH?

YOU WILL BOW DOWN BEFORE ME, CREATURE!

KR-AAAAASH

MAXIMA? WHAT ON EARTH?

THERE'RE BOUND TO BE PEOPLE IN THAT STORE...

THERE ARE ALWAYS INNOCENT VICTIMS IN BATTLE!

DO NOT DARE TO IMPUGN ME, SUPERMAN!

LOOK, JUST THINK BEFORE YOU SWING, OKAY, PRINCESS? WE CAN'T QUARREL AMONG OUR--

THWACK!

:UGHNN!:

WAM

YOUR *ONSLAUGHT* DOES LITTLE BUT *STIMULATE* ME, CREATURE!

MAXIMA WELCOMES THIS, FOR ONLY WHEN A *WARRIOR* FACES *DEATH* CAN A CONFLICT BE DEEMED TRULY *WORTHY!*

MAXIE'S REVELING IN THIS, AND *DOOMSDAY* DOESN'T SEEM TO BE SLOWING DOWN MUCH...

SLAM

GAROOM

...BUT I DON'T KNOW HOW MUCH *LONGER* I CAN KEEP *THIS* UP!

FOR THE *TIME BEING*, I'D *BETTER* WORRY ABOUT ALL THIS *GASOLINE* GUSHING UP!

HOLD HIM *TIGHT*, KRYPTONIAN-- MAXIMA WILL *NOT MISS AGAIN!*

MAXIMA! THAT *LIGHT POLE'S* GOING TO *SPARK!*

SPARK

100

"NOTHING COULD'VE PREPARED ME FOR THE SIGHT THAT GREETED ME."

"THE TOWN'S MAIN STREET WAS DEVASTATED, WITH DEBRIS STREWN EVERYWHERE."

"IT WAS AS IF A HURRICANE HAD SWEPT THROUGH... AND IN A WAY, ONE HAD."

"THE MEDIA HAD A NAME FOR IT-- DOOMSDAY."

SUPERMAN-- FRIEND--CAN YOU HEAR ME?

G-GUARDIAN?

WAS ALL *THIS* NECESSARY-- *THIS* DESTRUCTION?

MAXIMA--?

SHE'S STARTING TO STIR-- I THINK SHE'LL BE OKAY.

WASN'T THERE SOME OTHER WAY?

THERE *ALWAYS* IS, BUT THAT DOESN'T ALTER THE FACT THAT I'VE STILL GOT TO STOP HIM...

... AND NOW I REALIZE I HAVE TO DO IT *ALONE!*

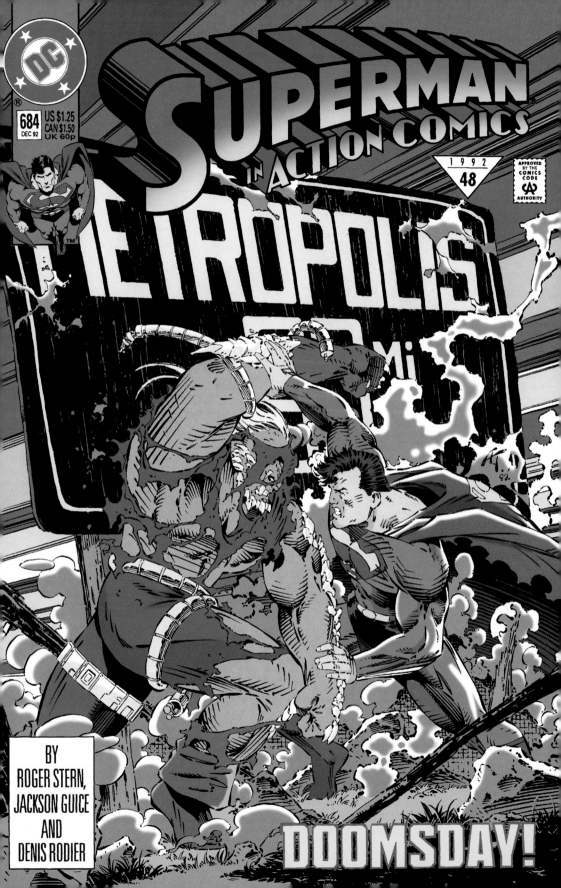

...DOOMSDAY IS NEAR!

A BATTLE THAT HAS RAGED ACROSS HALF THE NATION SINCE MIDDAY, HAS LEFT SEVERAL MEMBERS OF JUSTICE LEAGUE AMERICA SERIOUSLY INJURED.

THE BLUE BEETLE IS REPORTED TO BE COMATOSE, AND BOOSTER GOLD SERIOUSLY INJURED FOLLOWING... ONE MOMENT!

SPECIAL REPORT

THIS JUST HANDED ME... THE VILLAGE OF GRIFFITH IN UPSTATE KIRBY COUNTY WAS ROCKED BY AN EXPLOSION MOMENTS AGO, AS SUPERMAN AND MAXIMA FOUGHT TO STOP THE CREATURE-- DUBBED DOOMSDAY--

CAMCORDER FOOTAGE

--WHOSE RAMPAGE HAS BROKEN THE JLA AND LEFT A TRAIL OF DEATH AND DESTRUCTION BEHIND HIM. DESPITE THEIR EFFORTS, HOWEVER, THE CREATURE IS REPORTEDLY STILL ON THE LOOSE.

CIVIL DEFENSE UNITS IN CITIES ALL ALONG THE EASTERN SEABOARD ARE ON ALERT, AS AUTHORITIES TRY TO DETERMINE IF...

DOOMSDAY... MUST STOP DOOMSDAY...

PLEASE, MAXIMA... TAKE IT SLOW AND EASY. YOU'VE SUFFERED A PRETTY SERIOUS CONCUSSION.

SORRY I DIDN'T GET HERE SOONER, SUPERMAN.

I DOUBT THAT YOU COULD HAVE HELPED US AVOID THIS, GUARDIAN.

WE'VE NEVER FACED ANYTHING QUITE LIKE THIS BEFORE.

ROGER STERN
WRITER

JACKSON GUICE & DENIS RODIER
ARTISTS

BILL OAKLEY
LETTERER

GLENN WHITMORE
COLORIST

MAXIMA'S RIGHT... DOOMSDAY MUST BE *STOPPED!* HE'S A THREAT TO EVERY LIVING THING!

BUT SHE'S IN NO CONDITION TO DEAL WITH HIM.

GET HER TO A *HOSPITAL,* GUARDIAN.

I'LL STOP DOOMSDAY... IF IT'S THE LAST THING I DO!

MY GOD... LOOK AT THAT!

TRACKING DOOMSDAY IS LIKE FOLLOWING THE PATH OF A *TORNADO...* THERE'S UTTER DEVASTATION EVERYWHERE HE TOUCHES DOWN.

THERE ARE A HALF-DOZEN MAJOR URBAN CENTERS IN THIS REGION... OVER *25 MILLION* HUMAN LIVES ENDANGERED BY THAT MONSTER!

I WISH I KNEW WHERE DOOMSDAY CAME FROM...

"...I'VE NEVER SEEN ANY-THING--

K TOOM

"--ON EARTH OR OFF IT-- TO EQUAL HIM FOR SHEER BRUTE STRENGTH!

"IT WAS PAINFUL TO SEE WHAT HE'D DONE TO GUY GARDNER.

FRAKAMM!

"IF ANYTHING, HE'S MORE SINGLE-MINDED THAN DRAAGA WAS... AND HE SEEMS EVEN MORE IRRATIONAL THAN LOBO, IF THAT'S POSSIBLE."

GRAUHRRR!

"THERE'S A FRIGHTENING THOUGHT. LOBO'S GIVEN ME A HARD TIME MORE THAN ONCE... BUT LOBO'S POWER, HIS RAGE, DOESN'T BEGIN TO COMPARE TO DOOMSDAY'S!

"THERE'S NO DISCERNIBLE PATTERN TO HIS MOVEMENTS--"

MY GOD, THE OVERPASS HAS COLLAPSED!

WHAT'S THAT COMING OUT--?

NO! CAN'T STOP IN TIME! I'M GONNA HIT--

HRAURR!

--HIM! HUH? HE...?

WHAT DID--? HOW DID HE--?

OMIGOD... I DON'T BELIEVE THIS!

I'M.... FLYING?

"-- HE JUST SEEMS TO WANDER FROM PLACE TO PLACE, ATTACKING WHAT- EVER CATCHES HIS EYE."

RAURR?

THIS CAN'T BE HAPPENING. I MUST BE DREAMING.

THAT'S IT... I'VE DOZED OFF AT THE WHEEL. GOT TO WAKE UP BEFORE I HAVE AN ACCIDENT!

WAKE UP, CHARLIE...

...WOW... MUST BE NEARLY A MILE UP. EVERYTHING LOOKS SO PRETTY FROM UP HERE... SO... REAL.

WHAT IS THE MATTER WITH ME?! WAKE UP, ALREADY!!

FEELS LIKE WE'RE SLOWING DOWN. OMIGOD, THE CAR'S TIPPING BACKWARDS!

THIS IS NO DREAM. I'M GONNA DIE.

IT'S OKAY! I'VE GOT YOU!

YOU'VE GOT ME. ¿ HEH ? SURE.

POOR GUY. HE MUST BE HYSTERICAL.

SIR? DON'T BE AFRAID-- EVERYTHING'S GOING TO BE ALL RIGHT. I'M SUPERMAN.

S-S-SUPER...MAN?

NO CHANCE OF THAT, SIR. KEEP TALKING... AND TAKE LONG, SLOW, DEEP BREATHS. DON'T GO INTO SHOCK ON ME NOW.

I HOPE YOU'RE REAL... OTHERWISE, I KNOW I'M DEAD!

I'VE BEEN SEARCHING FOR THE CREATURE WHICH MUST HAVE ATTACKED YOU. CAN YOU REMEMBER ANYTHING ABOUT HIM... ANYTHING AT ALL?

"-- AT THE SHOPPING PLAZA ON THE NORTHWEST SIDE OF MIDVALE."

RUN! RUN FOR YOUR LIVES!

MY CAR--!

Lex-MART

MY KIDS!! OGOD, WHERE ARE MY KIDS?!

ATTENTION, LEX-MART SHOPPERS. THIS IS AN EMERGENCY SITUATION...

...PLEASE EXIT THE STORE IN A CALM AND ORDERLY FASHION.

H-E-L-P!

HEY, YOU!

URR?

YEAH, I'M TALKING TO YOU! COME CLOSER--

DOOMSDAY!!

URRGH?

KTOOM!

HOLY--! WHAT WAS *THAT*?!

I... I THINK THE RED-AN'-BLUE BLUR IS SUPERMAN. I DON'T *WANNA* KNOW WHAT THE OTHER THING IS!

AMSCRAY, YOU TWO! WE GOTTA EVACUATE THIS LOADIN' DOCK-- ON THE DOUBLE!

HAH-HA-HAH-HA-HA!

OW! THIS IS... INSANE!

I'D SWEAR... THE HARDER I FIGHT... THE MORE DOOMSDAY LIKES IT!

HE'S BEEN FIGHTING MOST OF THE DAY, BUT HE STILL SEEMS AS EAGER--AND AS STRONG-- AS EVER!

IF HE HAS ENERGY RESERVES AS EXTENSIVE AS MINE, I MAY BE IN TROUBLE!

WUP-WUP-WUP!

EH? 'COPTERS...

...THE ONE IN THE LEAD IS THE DAILY PLANET'S FLYING NEWSROOM--

"--OH, LORD, AND LOIS AND JIMMY ARE ON BOARD! I HOPE THE PILOT KEEPS HIS DISTANCE!"

THAT'S DOOMSDAY? WOW. HE'S A BIG ONE!

VERY BIG. BE CAREFUL, CLARK.

"...THE MIDVALE LEX-MART STOOD IN RUINS AS SUPERMAN STRUGGLED WITH THE MYSTERIOUS CREATURE." END OF PARAGRAPH...

"... STAND BY FOR MORE."

WLEX LIVE

WELL, MY *NEWS DIRECTOR* ASSURED ME THAT HE'D DIS-PATCHED A CAMERA CREW TO GET TO THE BOTTOM OF THIS DOOMSDAY *NONSENSE*...

...SO *YOU* WON'T GO CHASING OFF AFTER IT, LIKE YOU DID DURING THAT *SATANUS* AFFAIR.

IT'S NOT NONSENSE, LEX! THEY'RE ON THE AIR *NOW*-- DOOMS-DAY JUST WRECKED ONE OF YOUR *SHOPPING MARTS*!

WHAT?! BLOODY HELL!

SUPERMAN'S *TRYING* TO STOP THE CREATURE, BUT HE'S NOT HAVING MUCH LUCK.

ANYTHING THAT CAN GIVE SUPERMAN THAT HARD A FIGHT MUST BE INCREDIBLY POWERFUL! I'D BETTER GO HELP--!

WE'VE BEEN ALL THROUGH THAT, LOVE! THE *LAST* THING WE NEED NOW IS FOR YOU TO GO FLYING OFF! WHENEVER SUPERMAN'S AWAY, THE LOCAL CITIZENRY START GETTING... *EDGY*...

... I DON'T LIKE IT, BUT I CAN'T DENY IT--

--AND WITH THE OL' BOY OFF HAVIN' A GO-ROUND WITH SOME UGLY *DRONGO*, THE CITY NEEDS ITS *SUPERGIRL* TO FILL THE VOID.

ARE YOU *SURE*, LEX? DOOMSDAY'S ALREADY CAUSED SO MUCH DESTRUCTION. AND YOUR NEWSMAN PLACED THE LATEST *DEATH TOLL* AT OVER A HUNDRED!

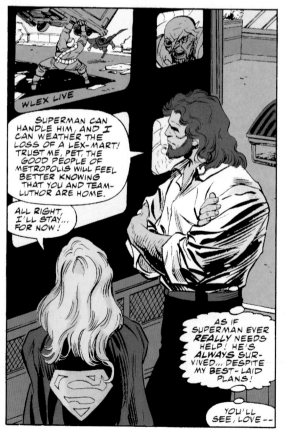

WLEX LIVE

SUPERMAN CAN HANDLE HIM, AND *I* CAN WEATHER THE LOSS OF A LEX-MART! TRUST ME, PET, THE GOOD PEOPLE OF METROPOLIS WILL FEEL BETTER KNOWING THAT YOU AND TEAM-LUTHOR ARE HOME.

ALL RIGHT, I'LL STAY... FOR NOW!

AS IF SUPERMAN EVER *REALLY* NEEDS HELP! HE'S *ALWAYS* SUR-VIVED.... DESPITE MY BEST-LAID PLANS!

YOU'LL SEE, LOVE --

"--SUPERMAN WILL BE JUST FINE!"

"THEIR BATTLE RAGED ON ACROSS THE REAR LOT OF A FAST FOOD RESTAURANT, WHERE-- OMIGOD!"

Welcome to

jBe

BURGI

BUS PARKI

"UH... WHERE D-DOOMSDAY HURLED A PARKED BUS AT THE MAN OF STEEL..."

"...KNOCKING HIM THROUGH THE SIDE OF A BUILDING."

LOOK OUT!

WHAT--?

INCOMING! EVERYBODY DOWN!

HAH-HA!

AT LEAST... THE BUS... WAS EMPTY. BUT... ALL THOSE PEOPLE... INSIDE THE RESTAURANT--! HOPE THEY'RE... ALL RIGHT.

GOT TO... PULL MYSELF... TOGETHER.

GOT TO... END THIS...

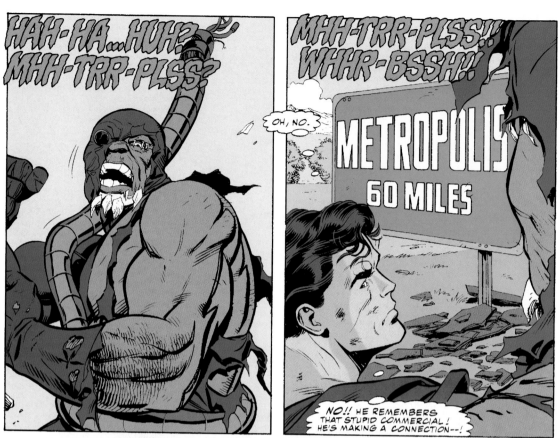

GEEZ! SUPERMAN MUST'VE GOTTEN A SECOND WIND OR SOMETHING! I'VE NEVER SEEN HIM FIGHT SO HARD!

N-NEITHER HAVE I, JIMMY!

NEXT PARAGRAPH... "TAKING ADVANTAGE OF THE CREATURE'S MOMENTARY DISTRACTION --

"-- SUPERMAN REDOUBLED HIS EFFORTS..."

GOT TO KEEP HIM OFF-BALANCE -- AND AVOID HIS REACH! HE MUST WEIGH CLOSE TO A TON...

...GOT TO USE THAT WEIGHT... BUILD UP ENOUGH MOMENTUM...

...TO HURL HIM AWAY FROM HERE... AWAY FROM METROPOLIS!

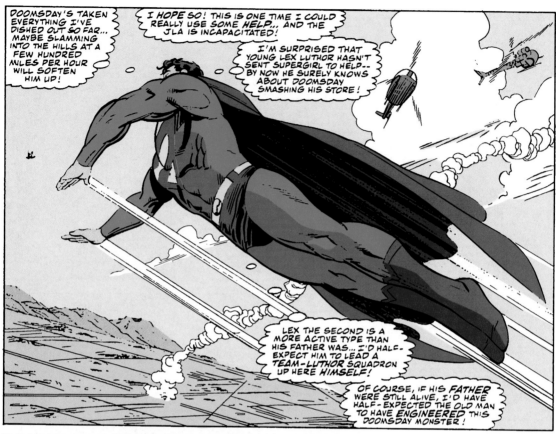

DOOMSDAY'S TAKEN EVERYTHING I'VE DISHED OUT SO FAR... MAYBE SLAMMING INTO THE HILLS AT A FEW HUNDRED MILES PER HOUR WILL SOFTEN HIM UP!

I HOPE SO! THIS IS ONE TIME I COULD REALLY USE SOME *HELP*... AND THE JLA IS INCAPACITATED!

I'M SURPRISED THAT YOUNG LEX LUTHOR HASN'T SENT SUPERGIRL TO HELP-- BY NOW HE SURELY KNOWS ABOUT DOOMSDAY SMASHING HIS STORE!

LEX THE SECOND IS A MORE ACTIVE TYPE THAN HIS FATHER WAS... I'D HALF-EXPECT HIM TO LEAD A *TEAM-LUTHOR* SQUADRON UP HERE *HIMSELF*!

OF COURSE, IF HIS *FATHER* WERE STILL ALIVE, I'D HAVE HALF-EXPECTED THE OLD MAN TO HAVE *ENGINEERED* THIS DOOMSDAY MONSTER!

I DON'T KNOW IF I CAN CATCH UP WITH THEM, MS. LANE, NOT AS FAST AS THEY'RE GOING!

JUST DO YOUR BEST, GARRET.

METROPOLIS ISN'T THAT FAR... I'LL BET SUPER-MAN'S TRYING TO KEEP DOOMSDAY AWAY FROM THE CITY.

WELL, HE'S HEADED IN THE RIGHT DIRECTION...

"... NOT MUCH TO WORRY ABOUT THERE. NO ONE'S ALLOWED MUCH UP INTO THOSE HILLS.

BUH-BOOM!

"EVEN A LOT OF THE *AIR-SPACE* IS RESTRICTED...

"...I THINK SOME SORT OF FEDERAL PRESERVE IS TUCKED AWAY UP THERE."

BUH-BOOM!

CADMUS PROJECT

@#*%!! WHAT'S GOING ON?! IS THIS AN EARTHQUAKE?!

INCONCEIVABLE! THIS IS ONE OF THE MOST GEOPHYSICALLY STABLE REGIONS ON THE CONTINENT! NO...

...THE PROJECT MUST BE UNDER SOME MANNER OF BOMBARDMENT!

TAKE IT EASY, WESTFIELD! WE'LL GET TO THE BOTTOM OF THIS.

YES...YES, YOU'RE RIGHT, JOHNSON... WE MUST!

THE GUARDIAN WOULD HAVE TO BE AWAY! THIS IS INORDINATELY INOPPORTUNE... UNLESS... YOU DON'T SUPPOSE--? NO, THE LEVEL OF COINCIDENCE IS FAR TOO GREAT...

"...AND YET, I CANNOT HELP BUT WONDER IF THIS SEISMIC DISRUPTION IS SOMEHOW RELATED TO THAT NEARBY MONSTER SCARE WHICH THE GUARDIAN IS INVESTIGATING."

UHHN... HHUNGH...

...HRRAARH!!

DAMN, HE'S STILL *CONSCIOUS!* ANOTHER SECOND, AND HE'LL BE BACK ON HIS FEET!

I CAN'T ALLOW HIM THAT SECOND!

GOT TO *POUND* HIM-- AND *KEEP* POUNDING HIM!

BROKK!

WISH THIS STAND OF TREES WASN'T IN THE WAY, BUT THERE'S NO TIME TO... *EH?!* THESE AREN'T JUST TREES--

--THEY'RE *STRUCTURES!* WE'VE TUMBLED INTO THE MIDDLE OF *HABITAT!** THANK GOD, IT'S ABANDONED!

I MUST BE GETTING *PUNCHY!* I WAS SO WORRIED ABOUT KEEPING DOOMSDAY OUT OF THE CITY--

-- I FORGOT ALL ABOUT THE CADMUS PROJECT'S RESEARCH ZONE EXTENDING INTO THIS WILD AREA!

RESEARCH... THERE'S A TROUBLING THOUGHT! COULD CADMUS RESEARCH BE RESPONSIBLE FOR THIS MONSTER?! LORD KNOWS--

* THE TREE-CITY GROWN BY CREATIONS OF THE CADMUS PROJECT.

"--THEIR GENETICS LABS HAVE CREATED ALL MANNER OF BEINGS."

I THINK MAXIMA WILL BE OKAY... AS HARD A TIME AS SHE WAS GIVING THE DOCTORS--!

NEEP. NEEP. NEEP!

EH? THE ALERT SIGNAL? NOW WHAT?!

GUARDIAN-- RETURN TO BASE AT ONCE!

WHAT IS IT, RODRIGUES? WHAT'S WRONG?

UNKNOWN. THE MOUNTAIN SEEMS TO BE UNDER ATTACK--

"-- BY FORCES OF INCREDIBLE POWER!"

THIS *UNNGH* IS *NOT* *OW* GETTING ANY EASIER! JUST HITTING DOOMSDAY *HURTS*... AND HE DOESN'T SEEM... TO HAVE WEAKENED... ONE IOTA!

HRAH- HAH- HA!

THIS IS... JUST WEARING... ME DOWN. GOT TO... CHANGE MY TACTICS.

MAYBE IF I ... HIT HIM WITH SOMETHING...

...Y-E-A-H... SOMETHING BIG!

HHUNK?

THESE SUPPORT COLUMNS... MAY BE *ORGANIC*... BUT THEY'RE *HARD*... AS TEMPERED STEEL!

WORTH A TRY--!

PTOOM!

GUARDIAN TO BASE! HABITAT... MY GOD, HABITAT IS *COLLAPSING* --LIKE A HOUSE OF CARDS!

AND *SUPERMAN* AND THAT *MONSTER* ARE SMACK IN THE *MIDDLE* OF IT!

I-IT'S BAD... I'M GOING IN FOR A CLOSER LOOK! I'LL KEEP THIS CHANNEL OPEN...

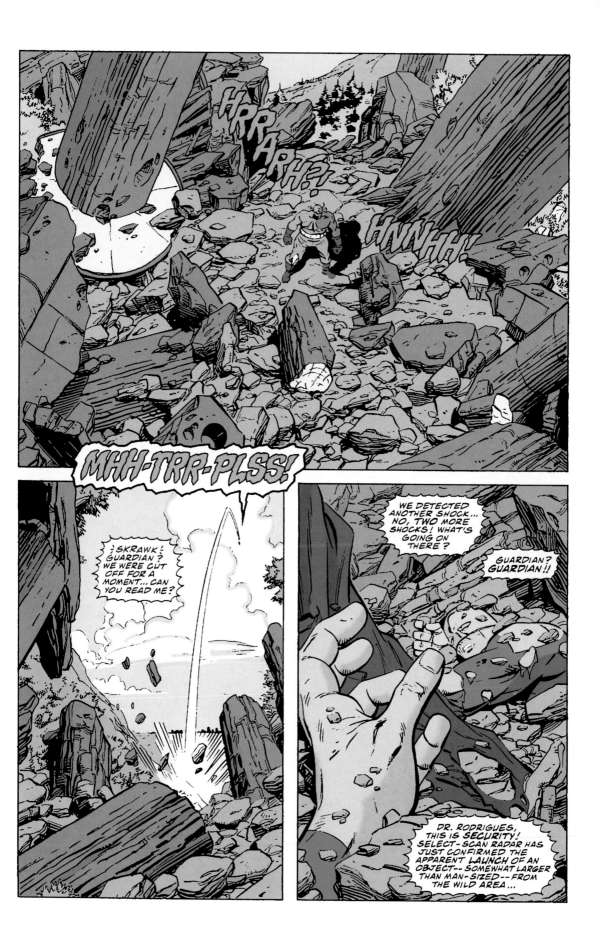

KLANNG!

"NEGATIVE, FRAN. THE PLANET'S CHOPPER IS CHASING DOOMSDAY AS FAST AS IT CAN...

"...CAT GRANT'S WGBS CHOPPER IS ACCOMPANYING US...

HRARRH!

"...BUT SUPERMAN IS ON THE CREATURE'S TAIL.

"KEEP YOUR HEAD DOWN, FRAN. IF OUR CALCULATIONS ARE RIGHT, THAT MONSTER MUST BE REACHING *METROPOLIS* ABOUT NOW!"

HURH?!

KLIK-WRRR.
KLIK-WRRR

AN' IF HE KNOWS WHAT'S GOOD FOR HIM, HE'LL *STAY* THERE.

I... HOPE SO, JOE. DOOMSDAY IS PROBABLY THE *DEADLIEST* FOE SUPERMAN HAS EVER FACED.

MAN, THIS MUST BE MY LUCKY *YEAR.* THOSE WERE SOME OF THE BEST SHOTS I'VE EVER GOTTEN.

DON'T *SWEAT* IT, LOIS. HE'S *SUPERMAN,* RIGHT--

WE'VE *GOT* HIM, FRAN! NEW *PARAGRAPH:*

"*DOOMSDAY'S* RAMPAGE IN PARK RIDGE WAS CUT SHORT WHEN *SUPERMAN* GRABBED THE *MONSTER...*

"...*ROCKETING* HIM AWAY FROM METROPOLIS, TOWARD THE VACUUM OF *SPACE.*" END OF PARAGRAPH.

"--HE'S GOTTA BE OKAY!"

GUARDIAN, ARE YOU ALL RIGHT?

DUBBILEX! WHAT... HAPPENED?

DOOMS-DAY SMASHED HABITAT! YOU WERE FELLED BY THE RUBBLE.

AND SUPERMAN...?

"--FOR THE DAMAGE THAT MONSTER'S CAUSED!"

WHACK

EVEN NOW HE BATTLES THE CREATURE.

I'M AFRAID DOOMSDAY IS TOO BIG FOR SUPERMAN TO HANDLE ALONE.

DOOMSDAY MAY BE ONE OF OURS, GUARDIAN, A D.N.ALIEN... A CADMUS-DABNEY DONOVAN CREATION.

TRY TO MIND-READ THE CREATURE, DUB. FIND OUT. I JUST PRAY THAT CADMUS ISN'T RESPONSIBLE--

CREATURE'S AS AGILE... AS IT IS STRONG! TWISTED AWAY ...COULDN'T HOLD HIM...

KICKED ME... CAN'T BREATHE...

THERE IS NOTHING IN HIS MIND BUT ANGER--

NO THOUGHT BUT DESTRUCTION.

THERE IS NO WAY TO TELL WHERE HE CAME FROM. NOT THAT IT MATTERS.

WE'LL HAVE TO WORK TO STOP HIM IN ANY CASE. IF ANYONE CAN STOP HIM.

LOIS, LOOK! DOOMSDAY'S FREE!

I SEE HIM, JIMMY! OH, LORD, WHERE'S SUPERMAN?!

THERE... I HOPE HE'S ALL RIGHT. NEW PARAGRAPH, FRAN.

"FAR ABOVE METROPOLIS, THE MONSTER BROKE FREE, HURLING THE MAN OF STEEL MORE THAN A MILE TO THE GROUND..."

SUPERMAN'S DOWN! GET CLOSER, BLAST YOU! WGBS NEEDS A SHOT OF THIS!

KRAZH

THROMB

136

140

MY LORD IN HEAVEN! HE'S THROWN OFF *SUPERMAN*!

WHAT-- WHAT *IS* THAT CREATURE?

I SUS- PECT IT'S A *DOOMSDAY WEAPON*, MILDRED...

...LEFT BEHIND BY *WARWORLD* TO *DECI- MATE* THE EARTH IN CASE THEIR SWARM FAILED!

WE FINALLY GOT DIS *LASER CANNON* SHOVED UP ON DA ROOF O' YOUR LAB, PER- FESSER HAM...

...SO LET'S *USE* IT!!

AS SOON AS *SUPERGIRL* GETS OUT OF THE WAY, BIBBO!

YOU AND MILDRED KEEP YOUR *FORCE BELTS* BUCKLED TIGHT!

WHEN THE CREATURE FEELS THE *BLAST*, HE'S GOING TO BE *ANGRY*!

BLASH

NEVER SEEN A CREATURE THIS *POWERFUL*. MUST BE SOME--

142

144

FOCUS YOUR FIRE ON THE CREATURE!

THE WEAPONS BOYS AT PROJECT CADMUS SAY THESE SHOCK CANNONS CAN TAKE OUT A *TANK!*

MOVE IN CLOSER! WE'RE BROADCASTING THIS *LIVE!*

HOW CAN WE HANDLE THIS GUY WHEN SUPERMAN CAN'T? THIS REALLY MIGHT BE--

LEXPARK 4⁵⁰
ALL DAY SATURDAY SUNDAY 5⁰⁰

ONE WAY

HURFF!

SKRAKK

154

156

159

163

LIKE WEARY BOXERS WHO HAVE GONE THE DISTANCE, THE COMBATANTS COLLIDE IN ONE LAST, EXPLOSIVE EFFORT.

IN THE YEARS TO COME A FEW WITNESSES WILL TELL OF THE POWER OF THESE FINAL PUNCHES... THAT THEY COULD LITERALLY FEEL THE SHOCKWAVES.

OTHERS WILL REMEMBER THE ENORMOUS CRATER THAT RESULTED FROM THE SHEER FORCE OF THE BLOWS.

BUT MOST WILL REMEMBER THIS SAD DAY--

Here Lies
Earth's Greatest
Hero

NEWSTIME

AY 1993

$2.95 US
$3.95 CAN

The Life and Death of the Man of Steel
World Without A Superman

Things Are Booming in Coast City

Experience the high life in the West Coast's fastest growing city

Beautiful beaches, four-star restaurants, and attractive real estate packages combine to complement Coast City's rising employment levels and falling crime rates.

Condominium Cartel™ invites you, for a limited time only, to visit the City of Dreams for three days and two nights at a 30% discount. Airfare and living accommodations at a cost too low to believe.

But wait, there's more! Decide to buy in one of our six Sea Breeze townhouse complexes and the other 70% will be applied toward your closing costs.

Things are looking up for Coast City!

Come for the Weekend . . . Stay for a Lifetime

FERRIS
AIRCRAFT

NEWSTIME

SPECIAL ISSUE

WORLD WITHOUT A SUPERMAN

FEATURES

DEPARTMENTS

COVER: Denis Rodier after James B. Olsen

JOHN BYRNE/AMALGAMATED PRESS

The Man of Steel flying high.

FROM THE PUBLISHER

A news magazine is only as good as the people who work for it. That statement may seem simplistic, but there's a mountain of truth behind it. The success of NEWSTIME has been due largely to its talented staff of editors, reporters, photographers, and researchers — all top journalists in their own right. Without their hard work the production of this magazine would be impossible. But no staff is ever big enough to cover all of the news. That is why NEWSTIME employs the services of various freelance news stringers and photographers, the better to bring its readership the whole of the world's events, as accurately and expeditiously as possible. It has been both our pleasure and our honor to draw upon the best of these outside sources over the years, and — in point of fact — many freelancers have expressed great pride in seeing their work become part of the sum that is NEWSTIME.

When the world was shaken by the sudden, tragic death of Superman, it again became necessary to reach outside the immediate NEWSTIME family to properly report his passing.

In this case, we were most fortunate to enjoy the cooperation of that great Metropolitan newspaper, the much-lauded *Daily Planet*, in assembling this issue. The *Planet*'s veteran photo editor Tyler Washington generously provided us with access to his newspaper's extensive photographic library and worked with Planet staff photographer James Olsen in assembling many of the images presented in this issue.

Of special note is this issue's cover, taken from a photo shot by Olsen as Superman lay dying. Of all that select fraternity who were fortunate enough to have photographed Superman over the years, no one has assembled a body of work to rival Olsen's. "Whenever I think of him, I always picture him flying," said Olsen, "his cape rippling in the wind." The red cape has always been a dominant image in photos of the Man of Steel, and so our cover recalls not only the hero, but also his sacrifice. May he rest in peace.

Collin Thornton

When the Wind Blows

IT'S ALMOST UNBELIEVABLE HOW LITTLE actual aid has been rendered to the unfortunate Quracis who survived the blasts that levelled their city. ("ILL WINDS," Mar. 9) Even in our shaky economic climate, is it really possible that an entire nation, especially one as poor as Qurac, could be left to struggle alone in the wake of such a disaster? Although aid has been promised to the Quraci people, the United Nations has failed to come to terms with the large-scale relief efforts needed at this time. Between the famine in Somalia and the Quraci disaster, the effectiveness of the U.N. can only come into question. What happens when it's our turn?

Michael Felden
Lancaster, PA

IT IS DISASTERS LIKE THIS THAT MAKE the abolition of weaponry, especially hi-tech nuclear weapons, imperative. It gets easier and easier for any two-bit terrorist to acquire weapons that create comprehensive destruction. Although the United States and the United Nations are offering support and relief for the devastated Quraci nation, no amount of money and services can possibly repair or replace the homes and lives that have been lost. The long-term effects of this horrifying occurrence cannot even be calculated at this stage. We can only hope that the demolition of all such weapons is accomplished posthaste, before the next psychotic sociopath steals our own weapons to destroy our land.

David Addota
New York

Stranger than Fiction

LIVING IN A WORLD WHICH HAS IN recent months successfully repelled two alien invasions forces us to admit just how little we know about our universe, and to maintain open, inquisitive minds. On the other hand, skepticism is not only a healthy, but a necessary reaction to the disruption suffered by NEWSTIME ("THE STRANGE CASE OF THE MISSING BUILDING," Mar. 2). If we believe that some men and women can indeed fly, then the temporary disappearance of a Metropolis skyscraper is not too far-fetched. While the sudden, tragic deaths of over a dozen people stand as mute evidence that something terrible happened, eyewitness descriptions of attacking "demons" and fantastic "nether-realms" could easily be ascribed to mass hysteria. To suggest, as your report does, that the spatial displacement of NEWSTIME's offices was caused by supernatural forces constitutes yellow journalism of the most criminally irresponsible form.

Dr. Terrence Thirteen
Cliffton-by-the-Sea, ME

NEWSTIME *stands by its story.*

New Guy in Town

YOUR ARTICLE ON THE FORMER GREEN Lantern Guy Gardner ("HERO OR VILLAIN?," Mar. 9) was chilling. No one, not even a supposed member of the Justice League, has the right to take the law into his own hands. Gardner's stated goal in leveling a city block as part of his so-called "War on Scum" shows not only his callous disregard for due process, property rights, and the public safety, but also his hypocrisy. It is a matter of record that Gardner has himself been a frequent, one might even say eager, patron of just the sort of theaters and bookstores which he so self-righteously destroyed. One must ask why he singled out the businesses on that particular block for demolition. Was it just the whim of

the moment? Or had they foolishly shortchanged him?

Paula Dean
Brooklyn, NY

SO, THE LIBERAL MEDIA ARE ALL upset that Guy Gardner wants to de-worm the rotten Big Apple. Why am I not surprised? If I were Gardner, I'd plow the whole mess under and head west! Come on out to God's Country, Guy. At least we know a real hero when we see one.

Buford Randall
Kerfoot, TX

THE JUSTICE LEAGUE HAS SURVIVED thus far with Gardner in their ranks, and will no doubt continue to function, either with or without him. I am fully confident that, should the former Green Lantern become too uncontrollable, the League will deal with him.

Lillian Foxworthy
Atlanta, GA

HOW DID GARDNER COME BY HIS NEW golden power ring? Once again, NEWSTIME has told only part of the story.

John Osgood
Tokyo, Japan

Golden Girl

IN YOUR PROFILE OF THE ACTRESS Jennifer D'Oro ("ALL THAT GLITTERS," Feb. 23), you fail to take into account that the steely determination that made her what she is today is the double-edged sword that keeps her from ever achieving any true excellence in her performances. Admittedly she worked hard to get where she is, but the same innate toughness that got her noticed in the first place prevents her from being able to understand, much less recreate, all the gentle and affectionate characters she keeps trying to play. She'd be much better off playing the hard-as-nails 1940's types she seems to emulate in real life.

James Medoza
Arlington, VT

We've Used What We Know to Rebuild the Planet

Superior Construction Today
Building a Foundation for Tommorrow

In this nation's largest cities the odds are high that disaster will strike at any given moment. Alien invasions. Failed experiments. Gas main explosions. Even good old-fashioned arson. You need a construction company you can count on when your world comes crashing down around you. We are the construction company you can count on. We are

SAMSON
BUILDING TECHNOLOGIES

364 President Street • Metropolis • (123) 555-5472

Coasting Along

HAVING SPENT MOST OF MY LIFE IN travel before finally settling in Coast City, I can say with some authority that Danielle Burd's article ("THE UNKNOWN COAST," Mar. 9) delightfully brings to the fore some of Coast City's more attractive features. Many people think of my adopted city as a mere sprawl of suburbs and businesses, and are not aware of the multitude of things to do and see here. The unusual ethnic mixture of its people, coupled with the state's liberal tax incentives to small businesses has created a richly textured environment. There are so many good and authentic restaurants, shops, theaters, clubs and other varieties of entertainment (albeit not found on the main boulevards) that it's no wonder that several prominent personalities have chosen to make their homes here. I have been all over the world, and can safely say that I have never found a city with more to offer. Thank you, Ms. Burd, for giving the world your "Burd's-eye view" on the City by the Sea.

Jake Ramirez
Coast City, CA

COAST CITY IS NOTHING SPECIAL. IF IT weren't for the movie stars and Green Lantern (and he's not around all that much anymore), it would just be a bunch of suburbs linked by Big Belly burger joints.

Andrea Curtin
Riverside, CA

COAST CITY SOUNDS LIKE A VERITABLE fantasy land of movie stars, quaint and/or trendy out-of-the-way cafés and glittering night life. Although it has a reputation for shallow affectation and ditzy blondes, it sounds like a truly fun place to visit (if you know how to drive)!

Crass or magical, big or quaint, any place that draws this much attention to itself deserves a trip. Whether the motive is curiosity or condemnation, so many visitors can't be wrong.

Kevin Whitfield
Madison, WI

Money Matters

IT SEEMS THAT ROB WILLIAMSON HAS it all: looks, money, women and fame. Could he be the next Donald Trump or Lex Luthor Sr.? They say that success stories like this happen only a couple of times a generation. Sorry, lads, looks like Lex Jr. and Rob have walked away with the honors this year.

Matthew Simpson
Utica, NY

Corrections

IN "TECHNOLOGY'S CUTTING EDGE" (Mar. 2), you make mention of a marine biology laboratory on Metropolis Harbor being operated by S.T.A.R. Labs. The supposed laboratory pictured in the article, however, is The Ark, a floating public aquarium jointly maintained by the Metropolis Harbor Authority and the University of Metropolis under a grant from the LexCorp Foundation.

Hermione Wells
Chancellor
University of Metropolis

I'M AFRAID YOUR INFORMATION about the broadcast media ("SUPERSTATIONS ON THE RISE," Mar. 9) is somewhat out of date. Although I still have several friends working there, I myself haven't been affiliated with the Gotham Broadcasting Company for quite a few years.

Alan Scott
General Manager, TV-18
Los Angeles, CA

NEWSTIME *regrets the errors.*

Your comments are eagerly solicited. Letters to the Editor should include the writer's full name, address, and telephone number, and should be sent to:

NEWSTIME Letters
c/o DC Comics
1325 Avenue of the Americas
New York, NY 10019

Letters may be edited for purposes of clarity or space.

PUBLISHER: Collin Thornton
EDITOR-IN-CHIEF: Fenton Madison
EDITORIAL DIRECTOR: Angela Dupree
CORPORATE EDITOR: Jason Railsback
DIRECTOR OF NEW MEDIA: John Moody

NEWSTIME INC.
CHAIRMAN, CEO: Natasha Udensiva
PRESIDENT: Henry Johnson
EXECUTIVE VICE PRESIDENTS: George Babiak, Holly Nakagawa-Pagels

NEWSTIME

MANAGING EDITOR: Terri Cunningham
DEPUTY MANAGING EDITOR: David Kaminsky
EXECUTIVE EDITORS: Dick Giordano, Joe Orlando
ASSISTANT MANAGING EDITORS: Sebastian Patane
EDITOR AT LARGE: Mike Carlin
EDITORIAL OPERATIONS DIRECTOR: Dorothy Edelstein
SENIOR EDITORS: Karen Berger, Mike Carlin, Archie Goodwin, Andy Helfer, Dennis O'Neil
ART DIRECTOR: Brian Pearce
GRAPHICS DIRECTOR: Robbin Brosterman
DESIGN DIRECTOR: Jim Chadwick
CHIEF OF RESEARCH: Jennifer Frank
PICTURE EDITOR: Ed Norton
COPY CHIEF: Joseph O'Hara
MAKEUP: Janet McEntee
PRODUCTION MANAGER: Fred Ruiz
SENIOR WRITER: Roger Stern
ASSOCIATE EDITORS: Brian Augustyn, KC Carlson, Margaret Clark, Kevin Dooley, Alan Gold, Laura Hitchcock, Bill Kaplan, Paul Kupperberg, Katie Main, James McCann, Stuart Moore, Jim Owsley, Scott Peterson, Tom Peyer, Dan Raspler, Rob Simpson, Bhob Stewart, David Tanguay, Scott Treimel
ASSISTANT EDITORS: Eddie Berganza, Ruben Diaz, Jennifer Frank, Jordan B. Gorfinkel, Frank Pittarese, Shelly Roeberg, Michael Sellers
REPORTERS: Aldo Ferrer, Tom Devine, Thomas Ward
COPY DESK: Richard Arons
BUREAUS: Michael Mayhew (Director of Administration) **Chief Political Correspondent:** Robert Jones **Washington** Herman Poday **Contributing Editor:** Martin Briggs **Senior Correspondents:** Reginald Van Gleason, Rebecca Cheevers, Sharon Smith **Atlanta:** Clancy O'Leary **Coast City:** Morgan LeFlue **Detroit:** Rondo Kandinsky **Gotham:** Heddy Flowers **Los Angeles:** Joan Moody **Metropolis:** Grace Milzoff **Miami:** Carlos Rodriguez **Brussels:** Joe Sprowt **London:** Archibald Leech **Moscow:** Steven Morrow **New Delhi:** Henrietta Jordan **Paris:** Barbara Bailey **Rome:** Victorio Shemp **Tokyo:** Mavis Yamamoto
ART: Dusty Abell, Brett Breeding, John Costanza, Rick DiMeglio, Kerry Gammill, Tom Grummett, Doug Hazlewood, Dennis Janke, Dan Jurgens, Denis Rodier, Rick Taylor
ADDITIONAL ART: John Beatty, Jon Bogdanove, June Brigman, John Byrne, Dick Giordano, Jackson Guice, Scott Hanna, Rags Morales, Michael Netzer, Art Nichols, Jerry Ordway, George Pérez, Joe Quesada, Louise Simonson, Glenn Whitmore, Mike Zeck
PHOTOGRAPHY: Joe Peluso
TECHNOLOGY: Rick DiMeglio, Curtis King, Brian Pearce
PRODUCTION: Fred Ruiz (Deputy), Ed Bolkus, Rick Taylor, Janice Walker (Supervisors), Al Aiola, Oscar Fernandez, Murphy Foglenest, Rob Gaines, Kim Gryzbeck, Ken Hill, Eric Kachelhofer, Don Lambert, Bob Le Rose, Arlene Lo, Amy Malcolm, Nancy Myette, Kevin Nash, Bill Scazzero, Cheryl Smith-Owens, Ilene Sternbach, Jamal Tate, Ruth Thomas, Darren Vincenzo, John Wren
ADMINISTRATION: Danny Alonzo, Cheryl Cramer, Jeanne Fong, Bob Greenberger, Mike McAvennie, Roger Rivera, Liz Seward, Judy Stachow
CREATIVE AFFAIRS: Neal Pozner, Pat Bastienne
EDITORIAL FINANCE: Patrick Caldon (Supervisor), Doug Cowen, Tom Pattison
EDITORIAL SERVICES: Troy Berry, Bernice Hollinger, Alyce Raeford

STAFF: Patricia Abrams, Alan Asherman, Maria Atti, Angela Auld, Francine Burke, Peter Burkle, Alyssa Cohen, Della Cohen, Christine Daniels, Marilyn Drucker, Shelley Eiber, Ruth Eugene, Barbara Farina, Ali Farrell, Linda Fields, Eileen Flood, Louise Furo, Angelina Genduso, William Godfrey, Judith Gonzalez, Enid Grant, Susan Hall, Maura Healy, Ed Herch, Marc Hirsch, Patricia Jeres, Ileana Jimenez, Bob Kahan, Sharon Kattuah, Jay Kogan, Steve Korte, Robert Leigh, Vince Letterio, Peter Luber, Eddie Marcano, Rich Morrow, Shannon McHugh, Art McKinley, Debra Mooney, Raul Morales, Mary Maxwell Murray, Eloise Olsen-Ecker, Eddie Ortiz, Marco Palmieri, Diane Perla, Robin Phelps, Patricia Pinkerton, Oscar Ramirez, Sandy Resnick, Cheryl Rubin, Karen Rydzewski, Charlie Salas, Len Schafer, Mark Silverman, Mark Thomas, Martha Thomases, Camille Truchel, Nancy Visconti, Bob Wayne, Brenda Wilson, Lydia Zamm

Investing in our future

In the Book of Luke, it is written, "Where a man has been given much, much will be expected of him; and the more a man has had entrusted to him, the more he will be required to repay." Words of wisdom that apply to us all. And today more than ever they apply to corporations as well.

As the nation's largest growing petrochemical company, LexOil has truly been given much. You've put your trust in us to provide quality gasoline, heating oil, a wide array of plastics and other petroleum products, and as a result we have grown and prospered. At LexOil, we believe that a portion of what we've received should be returned to the community, the nation, and the world.

Here's what LexOil is doing right now:

● Through our Invest in America Program, we're providing equipment upgrade discounts and matching funds to help repair and renovate heating systems in public buildings.

● Likewise, we're offering special discounts on heating oil to schools and hospitals and to citizens on fixed incomes. This year, we begin a pilot program to provide heating oil free of charge to homeless shelters in ten major urban areas.

● LexOil is a major funder of and participant in LexCorp International's Employee Wellness Program. The EWP stresses preventive medicine through regular examinations and improved lifestyle management. Through our comprehensive health program, we've made it possible for employees — everyone from the top executives on down — to donate unused sick days to fellow workers who are faced with a major medical crisis. We also encourage our employees to donate blood, to participate in bone marrow donor programs, and to enroll in first aid and water safety courses. And what's more, by using a combination of employee payroll incentives and company funded therapy, we plan to be the first totally smoke-free petrochemical company by the year 2000.

● We know that an unfortunate amount of food that goes to waste in most institutional kitchens. That's why LexOil's cafeterias have set up a system whereby they can quickly transport surplus food to nearby charitable organizations and community soup kitchens. Our company cooks have gotten into the spirit, regularly helping to staff community kitchens on their days off.

And that's only the beginning! Working through LexCorp and its subsidiaries, we're doing all we can to encourage a spirit of volunteerism and cooperation.

There are never enough good teachers, especially in math and the sciences. So we're going to make it easier for our scientists and engineers to take time off under a special program to provide "working teachers" for public classrooms.

We want to encourage people to learn. So we're going to be funding more apprenticeship programs and scholarships — for continuing adult education, as well as for the college-bound.

We'll be working with the federal government to find a way out of the current health care crisis.

And we're going to establish a national monthly award to the "Superman" and "Superwoman" who best exemplify the spirit of care and concern of the late, great Man of Steel. Amazing powers and a cape aren't prerequisites for helping others. We think it's time that simple human heroism be acknowledged.

Why are we doing all this? Will we somehow turn a big profit from these programs? Not in a financial sense. But we hope that a lot of you will profit from them. Because the better off you are, the better off we all are.

That's not just common sense. In the long run, it's good business.

ON THE WAY OUT?

Metropolis Police Commissioner **JACK CASEY** is taking the heat for the sudden rise in theft and violent street crime which has plagued the city in the wake of Superman's death, and City Hall sources say that Mayor Frank Berkowitz may be forced to ask for the veteran policeman's badge. "Fightin' Jack," beloved by the men and women on his force, worked his way up through the ranks from beat cop to Chief of Police, and was named Commissioner by Berkowitz when the Mayor first took office twelve years ago. Instrumental in the

TAKING THE HEAT: Police Commissioner Jack Casey

formation of Metropolis's Special Crimes Unit, Casey has gotten high marks from both state and federal law enforcement agencies, and was once considered a shoo-in to replace Berkowitz should the Mayor ever make his long-expected bid for Governor. But as out-of-town racketeers have moved in on the city, Casey has come under fire from citizens groups for what is perceived as the department's inability to deal with the growing crisis.

"It's tearing Frank up inside! He really loves the ol' guy, and would do anything to keep him on," says a source close to the Mayor. But Berkowitz, widely blamed for a still-depressed local economy and still smarting from a narrowly won re-election to a fourth term, is determined to put Metropolis back

MURDER-FOR-HIRE: George Markham, with Lex Luthor II (Inset).

on a solid footing. To do that, he will have to restore his constituents' faith in their police, and insiders say that can't be done without a new occupant in the Commissioner's office.

CORPORATE CRIME

The business world was shocked last week by the arrest of LexCorp Board Member **GEORGE MARKHAM.** The charge: conspiracy to commit murder. The intended victim, none other than LexCorp's own youthful C.E.O. Lex Luthor II.

"No one was more shocked than I," said Luthor, as city police arrested Markham and led him away. "I had thought that George was one of my father's closest friends. When investigators on my security staff suggested that he might be behind a recent attempt on my life...why, I couldn't believe it. I can hardly believe it still!" Markham, who had previously sought LexCorp's chief executive post, allegedly hired the super-criminal Hellgrammite to kill Luthor, paying the would-be assassin a five million dollar advance. (Hellgrammite had made an attempt on Luthor's life in recent months, said attempt foiled by Superman.) According to a statement given the police, Luthor — though hobbled by a broken leg — confronted Markham at the executive's home, where the board member broke down, confessing to his role in the murder-for-hire scheme in front of witnesses.

GRAVE BUSINESS

Rumors that **SUPERMAN'S BODY** was missing, perhaps stolen, from its Centennial Park tomb shocked Metropolitans this week, especially when those rumors turned up in the *Daily Planet.* All was denied by a spokesperson for the Mayor's office, who later suggested that the body might have been "temporarily relocated" while structural engineers rechecked the integrity of the tomb. Officials reportedly feared that recent underground flooding might have undermined the monument's foundations. Once some special

TEMPORARILY RELOCATED: Who is buried in Superman's Tomb?

reinforcement was added, reporters from national and local media, NEWSTIME staffers among them, were allowed to inspect the tomb and confirm that Superman's body still rests within. *The Daily Planet* has apologized for releasing what was termed "an unsubstantiated story."

THE DEATH OF

The Man of Steel Pays the Ultimate Price for Defending His Beloved Adopted City...Metropolis.

By **ROGER STERN**/*METROPOLIS*

He first came to us in an hour of need, when society had grown dark and cynical and it seemed that greed had become the American Way. He was a stranger whose heritage was that of another world, yet even the most jaded came to acknowledge that Superman was a friend to us all. In time, he came to be recognized around the world as our greatest hero. Loved by many, even worshiped by a few, Superman soared through the skies like some guardian angel, using his amazing powers and abilities to bring hope to those in despair. Rarely a day went by that we did not read or hear of some new and amazing exploit of this mysterious Man of Steel who could change the course of mighty rivers and bend steel in his bare hands. He seemed truly invincible, as never-ending as his battle for the causes of truth and justice. And so, the world was shocked when Superman proved to be as mortal as any man, dying shortly after stopping a berserker assault on Metropolis by a monstrous creature called "Doomsday."

Reaction to word of Superman's death was immediate. In a Metropolis still reeling from the aftermath of the attack which had claimed his life, vast sections of the city were placed under a dusk-to-dawn curfew by Mayor Frank Berkowitz, and stunned Metropolitans — many unable to make their way home — flooded into churches, synagogues, and mosques. In New York City, people began to gather at United Nations Plaza near the new Justice League compound. A little after 6:30 pm EST, League spokesman Maxwell Lord, appearing shellshocked, spoke to the crowd, confirming that Superman had died. "I'd never seen such a reaction from any crowd in my life," recalls Lord. "They went dead silent for what seemed like five minutes. I'd swear I could hear waves lapping in the East River! And then, the crying started. There were hundreds, maybe thousands of people weeping openly. One man sank to his knees, tears streaming down his cheeks, and a little girl

Opposite: Superman is cradled in his dying moments by Metropolis Daily Planet reporter Lois Lane.

SUPERMAN

JAMES OLSEN/DAILY PLANET

Superman tells decimated members of Justice League America that he will take care of Doomsday.

Although his work took him across the country and around the world — and even off of the world at times — Superman's presence was noticed most often in Metropolis. Criminal activity there had dropped noticeably in recent years, and local citizens had come to look upon the caped man as their own personal hero. So great was the perceived security of Metropolis that its population actually grew by nearly a million people during the time that it became known as "Superman's home town."

From the little we know of Superman's background, however, it is safe to say that Metropolis was not the city of his birth. His genetic ancestors were inhabitants of a planet they called Krypton, a world that astrophysicists believe orbited a red dwarf star some fifty light years from

hugged him, telling him that it would be all right. I'll never forget that if I live to be a hundred." As night fell on the east coast, total strangers came to the aid of their fellow mourners and, seemingly from nowhere, candles began to appear in their hands. That great public mourning would be repeated in thousands of towns and cities around the world — at London's Westminster Abbey, on the Champs-Elysees in Paris, at St. Peter's in Rome, at Jerusalem's Wailing Wall, within and all around the Sacred Mosque of Mecca, and in Moscow's Red Square. In Japan, the Tokyo Stock Exchange was closed and morning rush hour traffic ground to a halt as mourners packed the Ginza to silently watch international television coverage on giant video display screens. Not since the killing of John Lennon in 1980, the murder of Dr. Martin Luther King in 1968, or the assassination of President Kennedy in 1963, had one man's death touched so many.

While the world reacted to the shock and suddenness of Superman's death, it came as no surprise to most that he would meet his end in the act of defending the city of Metropolis. Long lauded by its civic leaders as "the greatest American city of the twentieth century," Metropolis had begun to live up to that boast, as the public began more and more to associate it with the Man of Steel.

the Earth. It was there that an alien scientist and historian named Jor-El, discovering that his world was dying, rocketed an artificial womb bearing his still-gestating son away from the doomed planet. On Earth, the womb-device yielded the newborn child who would grow up to become this world's most renowned hero. Little is known of his intervening years, and in fact, it was only in the past few that Superman revealed the secret of his alien heritage. From all accounts, this most American of heroes was himself apparently unaware of his true origins for most of his life.

From his unexpected public debut with the rescue of the NASA space-plane Constitution, almost a decade ago, to his final heroic defense of Metropolis, he was both model and inspiration for a new wave of super-powered mystery men and women. As the first costumed champion to truly operate in public since the legendary Justice Society of America disbanded under government pressure during the McCarthy Era, Superman's presence seemed to trigger a virtual explosion of independent crimefighters. From Gotham City's mysterious vigilante The Batman to Central City's Flash and the globe-trotting Green Lantern, there was suddenly a whole new generation of "super-heroes" in the land. Ultimately, five of these young new heroes — the aforementioned Flash and Green Lantern, along with Aquaman, the Black Canary, and the so-called "Martian Manhunter" J'onn J'onzz — joined together as the Justice League of America. "The original Justice Society was, of course, the inspiration for our founding," the Black Canary once admitted in an interview for *The Washington Post*, "but I doubt that many of us would ever have gotten into this business if it hadn't been for the example set by Superman."

Barely a month after the founding of the JLA, the Man of Steel was invited to join the new League. "He

Superman crawls from the wreckage to face Doomsday for the last time.

Doomsday had come for Superman.

gave us quite a helping hand on our third case as a team," recalls Aquaman, "and the Flash [the JLA's first chairman] personally nominated Superman for membership, a nomination I was proud to second." Superman, however, tendered his regrets. "He felt — understandably, I think — that his existing responsibilities would keep him from devoting the time necessary to be an active member. Even so, he stayed in touch and was always there for the League, whenever we really needed him."

In fact, in recent weeks, Superman had formally joined the American division of the newly reorganized Justice League International, and many longtime observers of the League had been encouraged by his presence on the team. "Over the past couple of years, the League had become involved in a series of embarrassing incidents," confided one high-ranking State Department official. "Frankly, it had become a bit of a joke. We had hoped that things would straighten up with Superman in the organization. Now...everything is in disarray." *(See related article on page 22.)* In New York, an unnamed United Nations source confirmed that, with Superman gone, "the future of the Justice League on this side of the Atlantic remains in question."

It was Justice League America, however, that made the first attempt to stop the Doomsday monster. Responding to citizen's band broadcasts and interstate police calls, the JLA caught up to the rampaging beast near a LexOil refinery near Canton, Ohio. Former auxiliary Green Lantern Guy Gardner was the first to engage the monster, but not even the incredible energies of his golden power ring were enough to stop the seven-foot-tall behemoth. Nor were his six teammates — Fire, Ice, Bloodwynd, Maxima, Booster Gold, and the Blue Beetle — able to do much better. Despite their considerable power, the monster smashed and pummeled them from one end of the refinery to the other.

While the battle raged in Ohio, Superman was participating in a question and answer session with students of Metropolis's Roosevelt High School, as part of a special live broadcast of WGBS's *Cat Grant Show*. Upon being informed of the Justice League's dilemma, he immediately flew to the aid of his new teammates. Booster Gold was the first Leaguer assisted by the Man of Steel. "Doomsday hit me so hard, he knocked me halfway to Pittsburgh," recounted an unusually somber Gold. "Superman saved me from a nasty crack-up. I remember warning him about the monster...that it was like a walking doomsday machine." As the two heroes descended to confront the creature outside a suburban housing division, Superman addressed it as Doomsday, unintentionally giving a name to his future killer.

Fighting desperately to stop Doomsday from leveling the entire neighborhood, Bloodwynd, Fire, Gardner, and Gold gathered by Superman to join their powers in a single concentrated counterattack. "Superman cut loose with his heat vision and Bloodwynd with those strange eyebeams of his. Fire concentrated her flame on Doomsday, Gardner used his ring, and I drained my power cells into my gauntlet blasters," said Gold, "but all we managed to do was knock loose some of his restraints! And then...well, I don't remember too much...all I can recall is seeing Doomsday charge at us like a big angry bull."

Indeed, Superman was flung fully half a mile away by the force of Doomsday's sudden attack. Still, of all the Justice Leaguers at the scene, only he remained relatively uninjured. With the rest of the JLA incapacitated, Superman was the only one left with enough raw power to stop Doomsday. There ensued a virtually non-stop battle which tore a swath across three eastern states for nearly four hours. Though joined briefly by an Army air support unit, various police agencies, and LexCorp's young Supergirl, the battle continued in the main to be a contest of strength and will between Superman and Doomsday.

As Doomsday smashed and bludgeoned his way through the Park Ridge borough of Metropolis, a battered, winded Superman redoubled his efforts to stop the raging monster. Skyscrapers toppled and streets buckled under the force of their battle. Bruised and bloodied, his uniform in tatters,

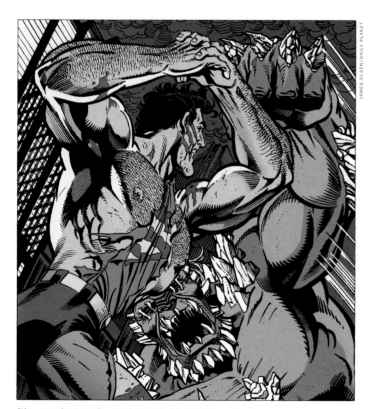

JAMES OLSEN/DAILY PLANET

It's one minute to Doomsday as the death blows are readied.

The world turned out to pay their respects to Metropolis's fallen hero.

Superman appeared to rally for his final face-off against Doomsday on the street in front of the city's landmark Daily Planet Building. There the creature and the Man of Steel hurled themselves at each other like unstoppable juggernauts. So powerful were their blows that they shook the city like thunderclaps, shattering windows in the immediate vicinity. Echoes were heard as far as fifty miles away. In the end, both combatants swayed on their feet like punch-drunk boxers, but neither would give up. Superman and Doomsday appeared to collide, each in one last, desperate attempt to stop the other. And then, both the hero and the monster sank to the pavement, still and unmoving.

Daily Planet reporter Lois Lane was the first to reach the side of the fallen Superman, who clung to life just long enough to hear her reassurance that Doomsday was dead. As officers of the Metropolis Special Crimes Unit cleared foolhardy onlookers from the area, the super-hero known as The Guardian stepped in to begin emergency resuscitation procedures on the Man of Steel. Joined soon by city paramedics, heroic efforts were made to revive Superman, but in vain. He was finally rushed to Metro General Hospital, where he was pronounced dead by Dr. Jorge Sanchez at 6:23 pm EST.

The great city of Metropolis momentarily ground to a halt in the aftermath, her usually efficient city hall all but struck dumb by the events of the day. It remained for the city's renowned young benefactor, Lex Luthor II, to take charge and fund a fitting memorial service for the martyred hero. In the days that followed, LexCorp subsidiaries rushed to clear debris from the city's main thoroughfares, as world leaders began to arrive to pay their last respects. The funeral procession through the heart of Metropolis rivaled that given any head of state. Those in attendance included virtually all of the world's greatest super-heroes and untold millions of local citizens. So great were the masses of people gathered at Superman's Centennial Park gravesite, that attending super-heroes suddenly found themselves providing crowd control. After a few uncertain minutes, order was restored to the milling throng, and President Clinton stepped forward, the First Lady by his side, to deliver the eulogy.

"Superman himself would...remind us to care for the many victims of Doomsday's attack," said the President. "And so we do. But how could we not especially honor the man who died to save so many more? His powers and abilities were amazing, but how much more amazing was the way he chose to use those powers! If there is a lesson in this, it is that the greatest power of all is our own ability to care about and help each other."

That being the case, there can be little doubt that Superman was the most powerful man of our time. We may never see his like again.

With reporting by Daniel Jurgens/Minneapolis, Louise Simonson/New York and Jeremiah Ordway/Connecticut Bureau.

WHO WAS DOOMSDAY?

Theories Abound
But Answers are Few

The moment the news was broadcast, telephones in newsrooms around the world lit up like Christmas trees. *Is it true? Has Superman really been killed?* The questions came in a torrent, threatening to overload the phone lines in many urban areas. *How could this happen? Why would anyone do such a thing?* At first there was shock and disbelief in the voices of the callers, a tone and timber that quickly gave way to sorrow, before turning finally to outrage. *Who did it? Who killed him?* Those who answered could offer little more than the name Superman had given his killer — "Doomsday." *Where did he come from? Are there any more like him out there?* As this magazine went to press, the most nagging of those questions remained unanswered.

Our knowledge of Superman's killer is rudimentary at best. We know from police pathology reports that Doomsday stood seven feet tall and weighed over a quarter of a ton. A succession of photographs and videotape images reveal a massive, gray-skinned monster of muscle and bone. "His skeletal structure actually protruded through his skin at critical junctures, particularly at the major joints," explained Doctor Charles Llewellyn of the Metropolis Coroner's Office. "Most prominent were the bony spurs of his arms and knuckles, and of his knees and shins. Those spurs weren't the result of any accident. I believe they actually grew through his skin, perhaps naturally...if anything about this creature could be called natural!"

Xenobiologists at Metropolis's new Scientific and

JAMES OLSEN / DAILY PLANET

Doomsday: alien, demon, or something else?

Technological Research Laboratories acknowledged the coroner's assessment, but were able to add little more. "While some of the bone spurs functioned as offensive weapons, Doomsday's semi-exoskeleton was mainly intended to shield and protect otherwise vulnerable joints," reported S.T.A.R.'s Doctor Milton Ehrenwald. "Fossil remains of certain dinosaurs have revealed similar adaptations, but I couldn't tell you how Doomsday came by his." Though S.T.A.R. has assigned a five-person team to study Doomsday, they've been able to make little progress. "We've ruined three sets of surgical cutters and a perfectly good chain saw, trying to make an incision," said Ehrenwald. "His body may be tougher than Superman's. We're reduced to analyzing saliva swabs and bits of hair. Frankly, I've never seen anything quite like this. I can't begin to guess where he came from."

Ehrenwald's frustration has been echoed in a score of hypotheses vis-a-vis the origins of Doomsday, many of them bordering on the fantastic. One sobbing woman the day of the funeral proclaimed that Doomsday had surely been the Devil incarnate. That idea has been echoed by the growing number of cultists who have recently been observed gathering in front of Superman's tomb. Originally based in California, this particular cult worships the fallen hero as the avatar of a living god and has definite ideas about his final adversary. "Doomsday was the Great Beast, the ultimate evil," said Robert Tierra, a cult spokesman. "Superman was forced to sacrifice his life to save this world from its sins...it was the only way the Beast could be defeated. But our great protector has not forsaken us. Superman shall return from beyond the grave to save us all!"

Slightly more down to earth is the scenario put forth by Utah's Hutchings Institute, a renowned scientific research center and think tank. Doctor Warren Clement, Hutchings's Director of Development, has suggested that Doomsday was a legacy of the Cold War. "We know that the Soviets had a number of projects — some dating back to the Second World War — aimed at genetically producing the perfect super-soldier. My guess is that Doomsday was the result of one such experiment that got out of hand. Obviously, the Reds tied him up and forgot about him." The Russian government, while acknowledging that a score of secret genetics experiments had been carried out by the former Soviet Union, has denied any knowledge of Doomsday's origins. "Well, of course, they would," scoffed Clement, "their so-called republic is still crawling with unrepentant Communists!"

More widely accepted is the hypothesis of Professor Emil Hamilton, a Metropolis-based scientific consultant. Hamilton, who had a chance to observe Doomsday firsthand, believes that Doomsday was not of this Earth. "Despite our world's remote location on the outer edge of the galaxy, we have known many visitors from other planets — Superman himself was an extraterrestrial, after all. I'm sure the partially successful invasion of the alien Alliance is still fresh in many minds," said Hamilton, citing the interplanetary force that established beachheads in Australia and Cuba

barely a year ago, before being repelled by Earth's super-heroes. "And who can forget Brainiac's recent attack? Doomsday might have been some alien exile or fugitive, but I personally suspect that he was some manner of living weapon, a failsafe left behind by Brainiac to eliminate life on Earth in the event that his main plan failed."

There is circumstantial evidence supporting elements of both Clement's and Hamilton's hypotheses. When Doomsday's rampage was first reported by Midwestern motorists, he was described as being enshrouded from head to toe in a heavy suit and bound up with metal cables that restricted his movements, suggesting that he had been restrained somewhere and recently broken loose. The cumbersome suit and metal bonds were largely destroyed in Doomsday's battle with Superman and the Justice League, but remnants gathered by the authorities suggest at least the possibility of extraterrestrial origins.

The Federal Department of Scientific Investigation has launched a special probe into the matter, and a field team headed by the DSI's Dr. Darwin Jones is currently occupied in the tedious task of backtracking along Doomsday's path of destruction in an attempt to discover just where he came from. While the world waits for answers, all no doubt pray for confirmation of Professor Hamilton's final word on the monster — "I most fervently hope that he was one of a kind!"

The monster's body defies analysis. Is S.T.A.R. Labs stymied?

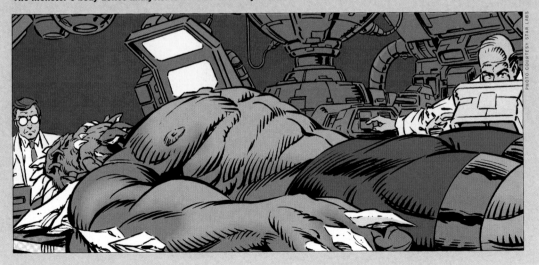

PHOTO COURTESY STAR LABS

DRIVE A LEGEND I
CAMELO

N YOUR OWN TIME™

DT 3000®

ARTHURIAN MOTORCARS LIMITED

IS THERE NO JUSTICE?

With Their Mightiest Member Dead and Their Ranks in Disarray, Is There a Future for Justice League America?

By any measure, it was an epic confrontation. On one side were the forces of light and reason. On the other was a monstrous killing machine, a true creature of darkness. They met in combat in America's heartland, and before the beast could be slain, a jagged wound was ripped across a third of the nation. When the battle finally ended, untold acres of land lay in ruin, the rubble of over three hundred buildings and the wreckage of nearly eleven hundred vehicles strewn about the countryside.* Tens of thousands of people were reported injured or missing, thousands more were dead.

---

* Early estimates place the cost of damages in the hundreds of billions of dollars.

GUY GARDNER: "I didn't much get along with [Superman], but...he did what he had to do. You gotta respect a man like that."

Among the casualties were the aforementioned forces of light, the battered heroes of Justice League America.

Ironically, the American division of Justice League International, successor group to the more famous Justice League of America, had just recently undergone a major reorganization. With the addition of Superman, the JLA was thought to have the most powerful membership roster in its history. The United Nations, under whose auspices the League was chartered, was especially encouraged by the leadership role which was being assumed by the Man of Steel. "We've had a few problems related to morale and discipline in the past," admitted JLA spokesman Maxwell Lord, "and the team had gone through a lot of changes. The U.N. naturally saw Superman as a stabilizing factor. Under his influence, the League did seem to become more focused. Now...well, we'll just never know, will we?"

Superman was not the only member of the JLA to suffer from Doomsday's brutal onslaught. The Blue Beetle sustained serious injuries to his head and abdomen and has remained comatose. Booster Gold's amazing battle-suit was shredded in the fight with Doomsday. "I expended every last erg of energy in its power cells, trying to stop that monster," said Gold. "Without the suit, I'm just another ex-quarterback." Another Leaguer who was weakened by her encounter with Doomsday was the former Green Flame, who had more recently assumed the *nom de guerre* "Fire." Fire was apparently so drained by the battle that she has been unable to generate her trademark verdant flame. Both Fire and her teammate Ice, who had broken an arm and several ribs while trying in vain to stop Doomsday, have reportedly left the JLA.

Although former Green Lantern Guy Gardner was observed to have sustained severe facial contusions from his encounters with Doomsday, they had all but healed within twenty-four hours. "Yeah, I'm tough," claimed Gardner, "and I heal real good. 'Course, I didn't take as many hits as the Super-Guy. I didn't much get along with him, but...he did what he had to do. He bought the farm, sure, but he still took Doomsday down. You gotta respect a man like that."

Also surviving with less telling injuries were neo-Leaguers Maxima and Bloodwynd. Maxima, reputed to be the deposed monarch of an interstellar empire, refused to speak to the news media. Nor was the mysterious Bloodwynd, a purported sorcerer, very forthcoming. When initially questioned as to how the JLA could go on with only three members — two of them tyros — he replied, "The League has a long, proud heritage. Its roster has changed many times. In one form or another, it shall survive." As if in support of Bloodwynd's claim, Maxwell Lord's office soon afterward announced the recruitment of four new members to Justice League America: Agent Liberty, Black Condor, the Ray, and Wonder Woman.

Of the four, the most renowned is Wonder Woman. As Princess Diana of Themyscira, she made her first appearance in the Boston area just weeks prior to the founding of what became Justice League International. As an emissary from an isolated island of Amazon warriors, Diana gained international fame from a world tour during which she preached a secular "gospel" of peace and

fellowship. Though a firm believer in nonviolence, Diana has often resorted to force in self-defense and in the protection of innocent lives. Though she has carried no weapons other than a glowing lasso, she is rumored to be proficient with a wide array of weaponry and has proven herself a master of unarmed combat. Her strength is believed to approach that of the late Superman, with whom she was once linked romantically. Given the title

WONDER WOMAN:
Amazon Warrior

"Wonder Woman" by a press agent, Diana has worked with more established super-heroes during times of world crisis, and was briefly associated with the European branch of the Justice League.

Black Condor and the Ray are two relatively new heroes who have previously operated mainly in the Philadelphia area. The Ray reportedly has a broad spectrum of energy powers and can fly at speeds approaching that of light which, if true, would make him a rival for the current Flash. In recent months, he defeated Doctor Polaris, the criminal alter

ego of the physicist Dr. Neal Emerson. Less is known about Black Condor. His ability to fly unassisted is obvious, but he also is rumored to possess some degree of psychokinesis. The Condor fought the notorious Shark to a standstill and ran afoul of the Ray through what has been dismissed as "an unfortunate misunderstanding." He has been very closemouthed about his past, facetiously telling one reporter that he had been

THE RAY:
Light Fantastic

BLACK CONDOR:
Winged Mystery Man

raised as a child by giant condors. There has as yet been no public acknowledgment of what, if any, connection the Ray or Black Condor might have with the World War II era heroes of the same names.

But the riddles posed by the Philly heroes are nothing compared to those connected with Agent Liberty. Though the Agent is known to have aided Superman in breaking up the Intergang crime cartel, and joined forces with several other heroes in the recent defeat of Brainiac, high-ranking officials of the Clinton Administration have expressed serious reservations about his membership in the League. He is reportedly wanted for questioning in the deaths of Air Force Major Charles Holcroft and Judge Ronald Kramer, two men implicated in the Sons of Liberty conspiracy. Pentagon sources hint that Agent Liberty may at one time have had a connection to the Central Intelligence Agency. The Justice League has refused any comment on rumors that federal charges may be hanging over the head of this new member. With the weaponry built into his protective battle-suit, Agent Liberty is seen by many as a logical replacement for Booster Gold.

AGENT LIBERTY:
Hero or CIA Spook?

The announcement of Wonder Woman's involvement with Justice League America prompted a cautious thumbs-up from U.N. officials. The recruitment of three relative unknowns was greeted with skepticism. Representatives of many Third World nations are rumored to be highly agitated at the thought that Agent Liberty might be a CIA mole. "The other two may be perfectly capable," worried one ambassador, "but we know nothing about them! Who are these people?"

A valid question. Yet similar questions were first raised almost a decade ago, when a young Flash and Green Lantern joined with Aquaman, a second-generation Black Canary, and a green-skinned Manhunter to found the original League. Can this newest League carry on the proud tradition of Earth's greatest heroes? Only time will tell.

THE WORLD REACTS

Fellow Super-Heroes, along with Civic Leaders and Cultural Figures, reflect upon the loss of Earth's Greatest Hero.

COMPILED BY THE
EDITORS OF NEWSTIME

FRANK BERKOWITZ
Mayor of Metropolis

WE HAVE LOST THE BEST FRIEND Metropolis ever had. I know that many considered Superman a citizen of the world, but in our hearts he will always be a Metropolitan. Our city has been blessed with greatness, and he was a big part of that blessing. We will never forget Superman. Never!

DAN RATHER
Anchor and Managing Editor,
CBS News

WE CAN NO LONGER SAY, "LET Superman do it." The quest for truth and justice must become our quest — not singly as vigilantes, but together as the great people Superman hoped we would be.

SAMUEL DELANY
Renowned science-fiction writer and
Professor of Comparative Literature,
University of Massachusetts

MYTHS HAVE A WAY OF HANGING around; and Superman is a myth. It's a Super-shame he's gone. But...

LEX LUTHOR II
Chief Executive Officer of
LexCorp International

IN DEATH, AS IN LIFE, HE HAS HAD AN effect on us all. I credit Superman, as much as my father, for making me the man I am today. I'm reminded of what Secretary Stanton said upon the death of Lincoln...'Now he belongs to the ages.' Superman has passed on to the realm of legend. He

is lost to us, and we must all learn to live without him.

WILLIAM SHATNER
Actor, Author, Director

WHEN I WAS SIX, I THOUGHT I COULD fly. I mean, why not, Superman could. So I took my towel and tucked it in the back of my T-shirt — that was my cape — stood atop the dresser in my parents' bedroom and leapt for the skies. When I returned from the hospital, reality had crash-landed. I'm sorry to hear that reality crash-landed on Superman as well.

BRUCE WAYNE
Chairman of the Board of
Wayne Enterprises

I ONCE HAD OCCASION TO OBSERVE Superman in action, and I can tell you that there never was a more capable man. There was something about him...something very good and noble...you knew that you could trust Superman. Some have called him naive and overly optimistic, but I saw in him an idealist, determined to do all he could to improve our world. What higher goals could there be?

BRAD ROBERTS
Lead singer of The Crash Test
Dummies, author of
Superman's Song

WHEN SUPERMAN'S SONG FIRST started to get a lot of airplay, people asked: Who is this Solomon Grundy character from whom Superman saved the world? I began to receive

PHOTO: GUICE RODIER

"I credit Superman, as much as my father, for making me the man I am today."

LEX LUTHOR II

letters containing the wildest speculation on this matter: one particularly adventurous theorist suggested that Grundy was a symbol of miserable existential solitude and Superman one of progressive western humanism. The shamefully banal truth of the matter, however, was that I simply couldn't find anything else that rhymed with the word "money" which appears in the line just preceding Grundy's entrance. But I kept my mouth shut, and bided my time as I waited for my first royalty cheque.

PENN JILETTE
Magician, comic, co-author *Penn & Teller's How to Play with Your Food*

HE'LL HAVE TO DIE IN A FEW MORE media before we're impressed. Penn and Teller have died in feature films, *Miami Vice,* TV specials and on stage (in more ways than one).

CATHERINE GRANT
Daily Planet columnist and host of Galaxy Broadcasting's *The Cat Grant Show*

SUPERMAN SO SELDOM SPOKE ON THE record, it was a real coup getting him on my show. I just never thought that it would be his last interview. He meant so much to so many people...we'll probably never know how many lives he touched. If not for him, I probably wouldn't have my son with me today.

JOHN GOODMAN
Actor

UPON HEARING THE TRAGIC NEWS I roamed the city streets aimlessly, heedless of noise, traffic, people. Nothing mattered. After what must have been hours, I found myself in the darkened theatre district. Half a block away was the oddest of sights: it was none other than Mr. Mxyzptlk operating a frank wagon

next to a peep show. He sat on the cart's bun warmer alternating deep sobs with hellish giggles and digging in his pockets for something I'm sure was not there. The nefarious pixie had been unemployed for weeks so I thought I'd throw some business his way. Plus all my aimless roaming had made me hungry.

I ordered two pups with the works and as he plied his trade I pulled out a cheroot and dug for a light. "Hey — got a match?" He looked at me with crazed red eyes and said, "Not since Superman died!" He doubled over in hysterical paroxysms of laughter and a wet hacking cough. "I've been waiting to say that for years."

I would have cuffed the tiny cur, but pity stayed my hand. Instead I gave him just the teensiest shove into the open weenie well and shut the hatch. When I opened it the acidy brine had done the trick. Nothing was left but franks, a yellowy film and a tiny derby. I had rid the Man of Steel of an old enemy, unfortunately a little too late.

But darn it, I felt better.

ERIC LUSTBADER
Author

DEAR SUPERMAN, NOW YOU BELONG to the simpler days of our childhood. Dream on, old friend!

DOCTOR WILL MAGNUS
renowned roboticist, creator of the Metal Men

I HAVE KNOWN OTHER INDIVIDUALS who had amazing powers and abilities, but none of them possessed as keen an intellect as did Superman. His capacity for learning and reason always impressed me far more than his raw power. Had he devoted his life to the sciences, I have no doubt that he

"You knew that you could trust Superman."

BRUCE WAYNE

"If not for him, I probably wouldn't have my son with me today."

CATHERINE GRANT

"His capacity for learning and reason always impressed me far more than his raw power."

DOCTOR WILL MAGNUS

"Superman could have ruled the world, but that kind of power held no interest for him."

WONDER WOMAN

could have been another Einstein. That he made helping humanity his life's work, and that he did it so very well, is further testimony to the greatness of his mind.

SHAQUILLE O'NEAL
Center, Orlando Magic

THE LEGEND OF SUPERMAN WILL always live on. Superman proudly wore the "S" on his chest, and, in trying to follow in his footsteps, I proudly wear the "S" (Shaquille) on my back.

BUCK HENRY
Writer, actor, humorist

ONCE UPON A TIME, DURING A National Media Convention, I found myself seated next to Clark Kent at the bar of the Kit Kat Klub in downtown Metropolis. After ingesting a number of alcoholic beverages, including one or two of the Kit Kat's celebrated Krypton Kocktails, Kent and I fell into a discussion of contemporary men and women whom we had met, admired and tried to emulate in our own lives. I remember mentioning, among others, Gandhi, Babe Ruth, Red Skelton and Superman. (I have to confess that I lied about having met Red Skelton.) Kent snorted derisively at Superman's name and, in a manner distinctly unmild, turned to me and said: "I know Superman — Superman is a friend of mine — and believe me — you're no Superman." Irked, I decked him. Knowing what I know now, I regret the entire incident.

DR. KAREN LOU FAULKNER
Director of S.T.A.R. Labs/Metropolis

HE WAS A VERY COMPASSIONATE man who went out of his way to shield and protect people. Superman was a friend to everyone

he met. His only enemies were those who made him an enemy. He set a standard we would all do well to emulate.

BILL PLYMPTON
Animator

AS WE RISE EACH MORNING, THE AIR smells a bit staler, the sun shines less brilliantly. The fine line between Good and Evil has grown shaky. We have lost Superman. Though our hero is gone, we have his example to live by. His courage. His ability to see through the murky smoke of human charades to extinguish wrongdoing in all its forms, all the while never overlooking the fragility of human existence. Now we must forge onward, laying aside our tears to continue the mission of Superman: the unrelenting pursuit of justice. Superman would have wanted it that way.

WONDER WOMAN

SUPERMAN COULD HAVE RULED THE world, but that kind of power held no interest for him. He was a man of great principle...the most respectable, and most respected, man I had ever met. In my travels around the world, I found that he was loved literally by millions. And even those who did not love him respected him. We are all the poorer for his passing.

LARRY NIVEN
Noted science-fiction writer

I WORRIED THAT HE COULDN'T reproduce his kind. It seemed there must be a solution, but I didn't see the urgency. Now I'm having serious trouble believing that he died in a mugging. He didn't seem the type.

MUSICIAN, HEAL THYSELF

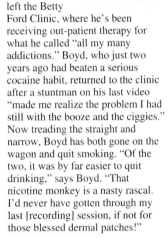

There was a self-effacing grin and a gentle wave from rocker **SPENCER BOYD** last week as he left the Betty Ford Clinic, where he's been receiving out-patient therapy for what he called "all my many addictions." Boyd, who just two years ago had beaten a serious cocaine habit, returned to the clinic after a stuntman on his last video "made me realize the problem I had still with the booze and the ciggies." Now treading the straight and narrow, Boyd has both gone on the wagon and quit smoking. "Of the two, it was by far easier to quit drinking," says Boyd. "That nicotine monkey is a nasty rascal. I'd never have gotten through my last [recording] session, if not for those blessed dermal patches!"

THE WOMAN BEHIND THE TUBE

The National Association of Broadcasters has announced plans to honor Scott Broadcasting's **MOLLY MAYNE-SCOTT** for her work in promoting better news coverage of community and minority issues.

Mayne-Scott, Station Manager of Los Angeles's TV-18, modestly dismissed the NAB's description of her as a "television pioneer." "I can't deny that I was around for TV's diaper days," laughed Mayne-Scott, "but I was just a studio intern at the Gotham Broadcast Center back then!"

ALL ABOUT THE GIRL WHO CAME TO STAY...

Despite the funereal depression that has gripped Metropolis, that city is abuzz over the activities of **SUPERGIRL.** LexCorp's highly promoted "Girl of Steel" is certainly living up to her press releases, maintaining a constant presence in the city's skies and lending her considerable physical might to Metropolis's ongoing efforts to rescue those trapped in the rubble of buildings destroyed by Doomsday. Like the late hero for whom she was named, Supergirl has personally maintained a low profile with the media, even while the LexCorp public relations machine continues to tout her as the cornerstone of an expanded Team Luthor.

NOT SO HAPPY TOGETHER?

Production delays on Galaxy Broadcasting's new **TURTLE BOY** kid-vid has already put that series into

a state of perpetual reruns. WGBS spokeswoman Laura Conway vehemently denies that the series' anonymous star has been a scheduling problem, but rumors persist of trouble on the set — both technical and talent related. Several unnamed sources hint that Titano's Pizza, the company with whom the Turtle Boy character originated, is not at all happy and might shop their creation to an independent production company if things don't turn around soon.

HAIR TODAY, GONE TOMORROW!

WHOOPS! Diminutive ex-jockey and former sportscaster **STEVE LOMBARD** (Stefano Lombardi) evidently got himself in quite a lather during a recent contract negotiating session with Galaxy Communications C.E.O. Vincent Edge! Poor Steve was perspiring so heavily when he rushed into Studio 7-A to host a WGBS disaster relief

telethon that an errant sneeze sent his hairpiece flying off his noggin and into the cleavage of celebrity co-host Daphne Dean. Losing his rug in front of a national audience is hardly Lombard's biggest worry, however. Tumbling ratings led to his being replaced as host of *America's Public Enemies,* and he is currently without a regular assignment. (Hey, Stevie, we hear that there's an opening on the Turtle Boy show!)

The Role of Beckman's Life!
CLUB
RED
SOCIAL DIRECTOR
VERNER BROTHERS PRESENTS
A MARLA BLOOM PRODUCTION AN ALAN MARKHAM FILM
JORGE RAMIREZ KYMBERLY MEADOWS AND INTRODUCING MORTY BECKMAN "CLUB RED"
WITH CAMERON POWELL AS "UNCLE LEON" MUSIC BY ELVIS NIXON & THE CO-CONSPIRATORS
EXECUTIVE PRODUCER HOWARD W. MAYFAIR STORY BY NORMAN BRAWLER SCREENPLAY BY NORMAN BRAWLER AND ALAN MARKHAM
PRODUCED BY MARLA BLOOM AND ALAN MARKHAM DIRECTED BY ALAN MARKHAM THIS FILM HAS NOT YET BEEN RATED
Rodier '93

MARRIAGE REVEALED. Melissa Guilden, 21, up-and-coming diva with the Gotham Opera Company; and Val Cohen, 23, drummer for fusion rock group Brigham's Rangers; last December 14; in Ivytown, New York, a Finger Lakes college and resort community where they had been vacationing. The unlikely couple had met in Ivytown a year before

when both had been booked into Ivy University's Turner Auditorium for appearances on consecutive nights. When not touring, they plan to divide their time between her estate on Gotham City's Bristol Bay and his Montana ranch.

RESCUED. Hank "The Hammer" Halloran, 68, former Metropolis Monarchs first baseman and Baseball Hall-of-Famer; from the ruins of Kovaleski's Gym after having been trapped for four days in the collapse of the building; in Metropolis. A renowned slugger, Halloran had a lifetime batting average of .331 and spent many years as a Monarchs batting coach before coming into conflict with Monarchs owner Grant Thornley. For the past year, Halloran has worked as an official greeter at Sultan's Palace Hotel and was recently appointed to the President's Council on Aging and Fitness. The wily Hammer gave a thumbs-up and drew cheers from his rescuers as he was carried from the ruins of the gymnasium, where he had been working out at the time of the collapse. Doctors at Metropolis General Hospital report that the Hammer is in good condition and should make a full recovery.

BODY RECOVERED. Morty Beckman, 29, gonzo comedian, from the wreckage of the Chatsworth Arms Hotel; in Metropolis. According to the coroner's report, he had been killed in the building's collapse, caused by Doomsday's rampage. Long a fixture at Metropolis comedy club Cheap Laffs, Beckman had just returned from the Bahamas where he had spent three months working on his first film, *Club Red,* a

farcical comedy about a resort staffed by former Communist guerrillas.

STILL MISSING. Clark Kent, 34, Pulitzer Prize-winning reporter for the *Daily Planet,* syndicated columnist, novelist, former editor-in-chief of Newstime; in the aftermath of Doomsday's rampage through downtown Metropolis. Kent first gained fame nearly a decade ago when he garnered an interview with Superman, the first ever published. His expose of the Intergang crime cartel was widely credited by police as helping to break that organization. Nearly as well known for his pot-boiler novels as for his syndicated column, Kent claimed to base his fictional stories of international adventure and intrigue on information gathered firsthand as a journalist covering the world scene. His third novel, *The Janus Contract,* was a best-seller, and his fourth, *Under a Yellow Sun,* won a National Book Sellers award.

RECOVERING. Lex Luthor II, 21, Chief Executive Officer and majority stockholder of LexCorp International; from a broken leg, suffered while leading his Team Luthor security force on a mission that succeeded in freeing S.T.A.R. Labs/Metropolis Administrator Dr. Karen Lou Faulkner from the hands of the terrorist cell DMT. Though outfitted in protective LX-20 body armor, Luthor sustained a fracture of the right tibia when a three-foot-thick section of the hyper-reinforced concrete ceiling of S.T.A.R.'s cybernetics wing gave way following an explosive exchange between Team Luthor and the terrorists. Claiming that he'd learned his lesson, Luthor promised to leave any further superheroics to Supergirl and his security team. "Once I get this cast off, I'm going to confine my urges for physical activity to horseback riding and handball, and maybe an occasional game of soccer," vowed the young C.E.O.

Unlikely hero, Buster Caine, is Courageous Man *again*.

Style Over Substance

TITLE: COURAGEOUS MAN STRIKES BACK
DIRECTOR/WRITER: RICHARD CURRY

By LEON MALTESE

When *Courageous Man* hit the screens three years ago, it caused a sensation at the box offices and a gold rush of merchandising. Neo-director Richard Curry was credited with turning a mildly campy TV super-hero into a near-mythic icon. (Never mind that he was running back over ground already trod by cartoonist/creator Bill Handy and a small army of successors.) The monumental success of the first guaranteed that a sequel would be made. Indeed, receipts for the first weekend had barely been counted when Verner Bros. began talking of *Courageous Man* as a franchise, as capable as James Bond or Tarzan of sustaining a whole series of motion pictures. When contracts were finally signed, exhibitors and retailers across the nation began rubbing their hands together in

anticipation of another, perhaps even greater bonanza. But the greed this time bears meager loot.

Courageous Man Strikes Back has little of its predecessor's charm and even less of its story structure. Admittedly, Daphne Dean turns in a bravura performance as the slinky Serpentyne, but a potentially electrifying cast is otherwise squandered, turned into little more than animated props for a shadow play of over-the-top special effects. The result is a motion picture that is long on style but tragically short on substance. Ironically, this comes at a time when Galaxy Broadcasting's animated *Courageous Man* series — again, prompted by the success of the first film — has debuted to both popular and critical acclaim. The animated *Courageous Man* backstops some of the most stylish animation ever created for American television with solid stories and deft characterization.

If there are to be any further *Courageous Man* motion pictures, one hopes that those in charge pay close attention to what's happening on the small screen. If we're lucky, they just might draw inspiration for a story that is truly worthy of the big one.

Too Sweet For Words

TITLE: SUGAR DADDY
DIRECTOR/ADAPTER: PEDRO FUJITAKI

By PETER P. PAULSEN

Just imagine what an action-adventure film would be like if written and directed by the late French auteur Louis Banal! If your imagination is even second-rate, you'd still probably come up with something better than *Sugar Daddy*. Comparing this execrable remake of Banal's classic *The Unbearable Sweetness of Existence* to the original is like comparing a first-grade primer to *The Brothers Karamazov*. True, there is the slightest similarity of premise between the two — and I could have

Super-star Gavone's all day sucker

sworn I caught one or two lines of dialogue that had escaped unchanged from the original — but *Sugar Daddy* is so preoccupied by its quest for ticket sales that any opportunity for depth, character, or even honest emotion is crushed to death beneath the wheels of its high-speed car chases! Director Pedro Fujitaki should go back to his music videos. They, at least, usually told a story!

Let's Get Metaphysical

ARTIST: JAMES ROOK
ALBUM: THE MAGIC'S IN THE MUSIC

By ALICE TOWNES

If rock has a true chameleon, his name is James Rook. From his early days as lead guitarist for The Electrics, through his experimentation with country and blues and his improvisational fusion-jazz work with the Brothers Marsalis, Rook seems hellbent on reinventing himself every two to three years. "My interest is in music, pure and simple," he once told Rolling Stone, "music of every style, form, and imagining! It's a little frightening to consider this, but...had disco lasted another month longer than it did, I might have been tempted to produce a dance album myself!" Oddly enough, *The Magic's in the Music* is the most danceable disc to come from Rook since the release of his first solo effort, *Unplug Me, Gridley!*, some twenty (has it really been that long?) years ago. Combining the eerie sound of Tibetan temple bells with drummer Gary Indiana's hot back beat and just a hint of theremin, Rook has gone to the mountain and returned with a disc that suggests a surreal garage band as created by computer wonks. From the driving introductory track "Embrace the Night" to the hallucinatory "Some

Forbidden Fate," there's an underlying edge to Rook's lead guitar licks, an intensity suggesting a man on a quest. Even in the melodic "Sing a Song of Sorcery," sung as a duet by Rook with Janet Jones, there's a sense of urgency lurking behind the sweet lyrics. Only on "Kickin' Back with Tark" does Rook allow himself to relax the intensity, but here it is for a bit of psychedelic rhythm and blues of the type you might expect if Chuck Berry had ever jammed with the Stones on "2000 Light-Years from Home." It's clear that, in whatever form he chooses to present himself, James Rook is the master of his music...and his magic! Once again, he's delivered both.

Super Session

ARTISTS: JOHNNY WALDEN & SPENCER BOYD
ALBUM: TWO GUYS SITTIN' 'ROUND, PLAYIN'

By FRANKLIN W. MAYNERD

Somewhere between Arlo Guthrie and Bruce Springsteen, Johnny Walden took his turn being lauded as "the new Dylan." Likewise, Spencer Boyd was forced to endure countless comparisons to Eric Clapton. With crosses that big to bear, it's a wonder that either Walden or Boyd

ever again ventured out in public, much less stayed with their music. That they have endured the highs and lows — the very lows in Boyd's case (see CELEBRITY, page 27) — and continued to grow past those "hot new flavor of the month" days is a tribute to the talent of both men. *Two Guys Sittin' 'Round, Playin'* will no doubt be compared to the Mike Bloomfield/Al Kooper super-session recordings, and perhaps even to the Traveling Wilburys, but any such comparisons are only superficial. Walden and Boyd have collaborated on eleven new tracks and a new acoustic rendition of Boyd's classic "Years Gone By (I Truly Care)" which are so wondrous that they bring tears to the eyes. Music this good has to be heard to be believed.

Back From the Dead

ARTISTS: THE DEAD SULLIVANS
ALBUM: A REALLY BIG SHOE

By J.G. MICHELS

What, you've never heard of the Dead Sullivans? Not too surprising. They were a college band that played small clubs and the opening act circuit throughout the Southwest before they broke up five years ago. But before the band fell apart, the Sullivans produced one album (actually pressed on vinyl, no less!) which ultimately wound up in the cut-out bins. But now, the good folks at Rhino Records have re-released *A Really Big Shoe* on CD with three extra bonus tracks, and the whole package isn't half bad. Oh, sure, the sound quality is often atrocious, the miking so bad that it renders the back-up (and sometimes, the lead) vocals virtually unintelligible, but there's a raw goodtime sound to these tracks and some not-too-shabby licks from bassist Phil Easton, who has gone on to become a much sought after studio sideman. Just think, if the Dead Sullivans had stayed together, they might have prefigured Nirvana!

MAY 1993 **NEWSTIME** **31**

The Mourning After

The only cure for lingering despair is in our souls.

Seldom has a single incident had so immediate an effect on the world as the death of Superman. In part, that can be traced to this century's electronics revolution, which by coaxial cable and satellite dish brings the world to us instantly, wherever we are. An endless string of territorial imperatives and blood feuds has become as much a fixture on the image orthicon tube as the infomercials and "reality-based" programs that seek to erase distinctions between what is and what appears to be. There has been a growing fear that Americans have become an audience culture, unable to distinguish fact from fiction, unable to react with true emotion to real events. That fear has been, if not put to rest, at least cowed by the reaction to Superman's demise.

Although their own camera crews were unable to get close enough, cable giants such as CNN and WLEX carried Galaxy Broadcasting's on-site coverage of the Man of Steel's Herculean battle with the well-named Doomsday. Thus were Superman's last moments played out live before an international audience. As many as 350 million souls may have witnessed his final triumph. Perhaps an additional two billion watched his funeral procession and interment in Centennial Park. On that day, nearly half the world's population joined in mourning a fallen hero, in witnessing the rampant hysteria of those closest his tomb. The passions of that moment were soon calmed, thankfully, and we were spared the sight of a worshipful crowd clutching at the coffin. Superman deserved better, as do we all.

But if the hysteria has passed, it seems to have been replaced by pandemic sorrow and anguish. A visible, almost tangible malaise has settled in all around us. Humanity has lost one of its greatest champions — a man who often stood between us and an uncaring universe — and it despairs.

It is right and just to mourn the passing of a great hero, all the more so for one who made the ultimate sacrifice in the pursuit of saving others. Superman in many ways remains an enigma to us. We knew little of his past and still know nothing of his personal life. In fact, very little is known about the private Superman. People knew him mainly by his deeds. Superman was the one who saved us when no one else could help, who time and again pitted his strength against the wiles of nature and the depravities of man. Millions of people are alive today, thanks to Superman. And he did it all without thought of recompense, always turning down reward and eschewing celebrity. "I do what I can," he once said simply, "because I can do it." Righteous without being self-righteous, he stood up for the dreams and ideals of the human spirit.

It is a tragedy to lose so good and noble a man, but we do him no honor by allowing ourselves to sink into the depths of misery and self-pity. Better that we strive to follow his example, doing what we can for our fellow citizens, both of this nation and the world. The pain of our loss will, never fear, be blunted by time. And that pain will be more endurable if we refuse to give in to despair and instead embrace hope.

Saving Grace: Hope has, to be sure, become a much evoked concept in recent times. The Reverend Jesse Jackson has brought crowds to their feet with the entreaty to "keep hope alive." And President Clinton was hardly the first candidate to rally voters with a metaphoric "place called Hope." But behind all the politics and the sound bites there lies a simple truth. "The miserable have no other medicine," wrote Shakespeare in Measure for Measure, "but only hope." The healing will come all the sooner for those who make their own medicine. Even in the midst of grief, we can find examples of hope.

Just this past week, Hank "The Hammer" Halloran was rescued from a collapsed Metropolis gymnasium. For those of you too young to remember, Hammerin' Hank was the steely-eyed Monarchs first-baseman who was tagging out runners back when present-day M.V.P.s weren't old enough for Little League. When the Hammer was located beneath the fallen masonry, word quickly spread amongst the rescue team. "I was afraid we'd found a body," confessed paramedic Joseph Orsak, "but then his eyes opened and he grinned that grin of his." Halloran is presently holding court at Metropolis General Hospital; attending physicians have cautiously predicted "a full recovery." How did he do it? "I was alive," said the Hall-of-Famer. "It didn't make any sense to give up, long as I was still breathing." A sixty-eight-year-old man, trapped for four days under tons of rubble, and he never lost hope. It's enough to make you want to cheer.

Here, there, and everywhere, a red-caped figure has been seen in the heavens. But that's no ghost haunting Metropolis's skies; it's Supergirl! That young lady has not merely worn the colors of the late champion, she has pledged herself to carrying on the never-ending battle for truth and justice in his honor. She has made a very good start, lending her considerable strength and endurance to city rescue efforts. And Supergirl is not alone. There are still dozens of superhuman crusaders, from Captain Marvel to Wonder Woman, actively working to make this world a better, safer place. But we must not, and we need not, rely solely on the men and women in the colorful costumes. There are heroes — ordinary, yet uncommon people — who live and work among us, and they number in the hundreds of thousands. They are the firefighters, the police, the paramedics who selflessly put their own lives on the line for us. They are the doctors and surgeons who work to the point of exhaustion to save lives and improve their quality. And they are the teachers who reach out to instruct and inspire our children. They have been there all along, these everyday heroes, giving of themselves, seldom gaining fame or celebrity. Like Superman, they do what they do because they can.

But we must not allow ourselves to become overly reliant on any of society's uncommon individuals. We all have responsibilities to face, hard choices to make. We can wallow in our sorrow, or we can take inspiration from these heroes. We can let our spirits fall or we can look up and ahead. The future is, as ever it was, an uncertain place, but we are all headed there, together. If we reach into our hearts and minds and do what we can, if we follow Superman's example, then our futures cannot help but be brighter. And in doing so, we will truly honor the memory of a great man.

We can only hope.

Once Again #1
in the Skies
Over Metropolis

An Unchallenged Leader

The people of Metropolis deserve reliability, confidence and an organization ready to take charge of the changes lying ahead. Only one company has what it will take to be there for your travel and express courier service needs. Providing service from Metropolis to all points in the country and beyond...faster than a speeding bullet.

Look!
Up in the sky!

It's a plane!

It's Lexair's Daily Business Express Shuttle!

Man of Steel Dies Defend

By R. LOWELL STERN
Special to The Daily Planet

Superman, sole survivor of the doomed planet Krypton and our world's greatest champion for justice, died Tuesday on the streets of Metropolis, of injuries sustained in the defense of the city and her people. His exact age and place of residence remain unknown, though he is believed to have been in his early thirties and had long been associated in the public mind with this city.

A hero to the end, he died defending Metropolis from the monster known only as Doomsday, finally slaying that creature with his last ounce of strength. Despite valiant efforts at resuscitation, he could not be revived, and was later pronounced dead by Doctor Jorge Sanchez of Metropolis General Hospital.

An Heroic Presence

Superman made his first appearance in Metropolis nearly a decade ago, during a month-long celebration of the 250th anniversary of the city's founding. The then-unknown champion leapt into the skies over Metropolis International Airport before a crowd estimated at over half a million, exercising powers and abilities far beyond those of a mortal man, to prevent the crash of NASA's experimental space-plane, the Constitution. *Daily Planet* reporter Lois Lane, flying as a crew member of the space-plane, later filed her

James Olsen/Daily Planet

account of that ill-fated flight, referring to their mysterious rescuer as "Superman." In the week after the rescue of the Constitution, he returned to the city skies, attired in the striking red, blue, and yellow uniform which was soon to become known around the world.

Over the next month, Superman at times appeared to be everywhere in Metropolis at once. From halting bank robberies and defusing hostage situations to fighting fires and rescuing cats from trees, nothing seemed to escape his notice. And though he soon after turned his attention outward, and his remarkable powers to the service of all humanity, it was evident that Metropolis held a special place in his heart.

The First of Many

As the first major costumed crimefighter to operate openly since mid-century, Superman has been credited with inspiring a new generation of heroes, including the members of the original Justice League of America and its newer incarnation. Though never a member of the original League, he has aided them in combatting a number of menaces and had recently joined the newly reorganized group. In a rare statement to the media, the Batman said that Superman's never-ending battle for truth and justice "set a standard for all of us in this line of work. He brought out the best in humanity, and never hesitated to oppose the worst, no matter what the risk to himself. I didn't always agree with the man, but I liked what he stood for."

"He was a man of great principle," said Diana of Themyscira, the Amazon Princess more popularly known as Wonder Woman. Once linked romantically to the Man of Steel, she discounted those reports as "the wishful thinking of press agents and reporters. I was very fond of Superman, but we were never lovers. He was the most respectable, and most respected, man I had ever met. In my travels around the world, I found that he was loved literally by millions. And even those who did not love him respected him. We are all the poorer for his passing."

Last Son of Krypton

Long considered the greatest living exponent of the American way, it was only in recent years that Superman dis

Thousands Missing, Fear
in Aftermath of Doomsda

ng City

vered his ancestry was not of this
orld. This discovery was first
vealed to the public during his first
ncounter with the cybernetic assassin
Metallo. In an exclusive *Daily Planet*
terview, he later confirmed that his
enetic parents had been inhabitants
f a planet whose name was pro-
ounced in somewhat similar manner
o that of the element krypton.

According to Superman, the world
f Krypton once orbited a star approx-
mately fifty light-years from Earth.
There, he explained, he had been con-
eived and placed within a birthing
matrix, "a kind of artificial womb."
Learning that Krypton was in danger
of exploding in the equivalent of a
thermonuclear ignition of the planet's
core, his natural father sent the matrix
of the still-gestating Superman to
Earth via what was described as a
"hyper-light drive vehicle."

"By sending me away from
Krypton," explained Superman, his
father had saved his life and given him
"the gift of humanity."

Though he never commented on
his upbringing for the record, there
can be little doubt that Superman was
born and raised as an American, in
the best sense of that word.

A Legend in His Own Time

Although he never hid his face
behind a mask, as did so many of his
contemporaries, little is known about
the private life of Superman. Many
thought of this most public of heroes
as an eternal champion, but in fact
(Continued on Page A4, Column 1)

ed Dead
y Attack

HUMONGOUS "S" SHIELD APPEARS IN A KANSAS WHEAT FIELD

WAS SYMBOL CUT INTO WHEAT BY ALIEN ASTRONAUTS?

What appears to be a tremendous tribute to
the late "Man of Steel" could in fact be a
gigantic road map or marker for wander-
wayfarers from beyond the stars.
Researchers and local farmers
upon the scene seeking an
asked questions. C
nal for hel

Superman and all related indicia and the DC Bullet are trademarks of DC C...

NATIONAL WHISPER

SUPERMAN WAS A ROBOT
MAN OF "STEEL" WAS EXACTLY THAT!
Conflicting sightings range from "knight-in-shining-
armor" to "life-size wind-up toy! [story p.2 & 3]

"I SAW SUPERMAN PUMPING GAS AT A TEXAS ROADSTOP"

ARTIST'S DEPICTION

SUPERMAN'S SPIRIT POSSESSES TEEN

SUPERMAN SEEN AT SHOPPING MALL!
INSPIRES NEW HAIRSTYLE! [p.3]

ALSO INSIDE:
"MONDO BIZARRO"
SUPERMAN DEATH
CULT EXISTS ON
SMALL, PRIMITIV
ISLAND!!

Previews (February 1994) cover **Dan Jurgens** and **Brett Breeding**

Two illustrations by **Dan Jurgens** and **Brett Breeding** created for T-shirts.

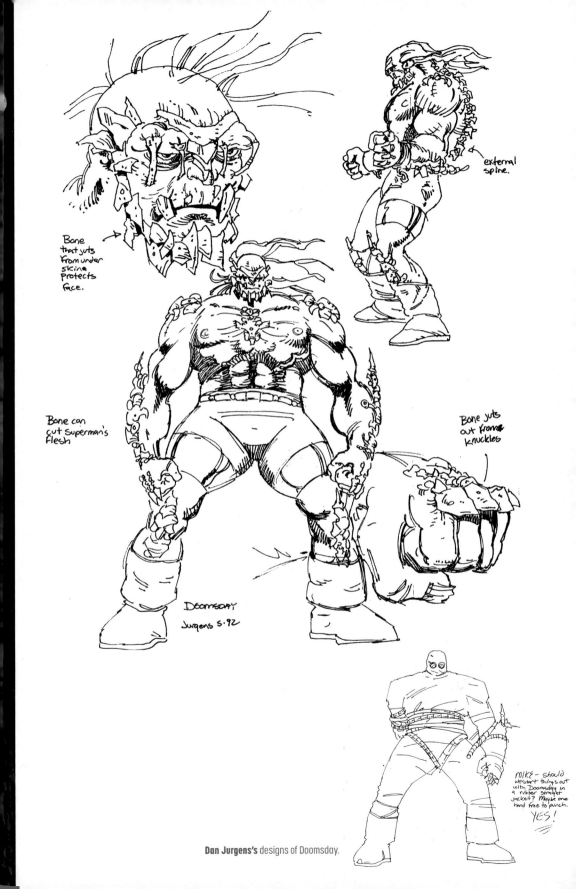

Bone
that juts
from under
skin
protects
face.

external
spine.

Bone can
cut Superman's
flesh

Bone juts
out from
knuckles

DOOMSDAY
Jurgens 5·92

MIKE - should
we start things out
with Doomsday in
a rubber straight
jacket? Maybe one
hand free to punch.
YES!

Dan Jurgens's designs of Doomsday.

MONTH	MAN OF STEEL # 19	SUPERMAN # 75	ADVENTURES # 498	ACTION # 685
JAN 1993	FIGHT HITS METROPOLIS. SUPES + D.D. BATTERED. {2 PANEL PAGES} F I G H T !!!! ①	**DEATH OF SUPERMAN!** "THREE MINUTES TO DEATH" {ALL SPLASH PAGES} F I G H T !!!!! ② FINALLY... ON THE DOORSTEP OF DAILY PLANET... SUPES MANAGES TO KILL DOOMSDAY... SUPES SAVED METROPOLIS... HE TOO FALLS DOWN DEAD. JO. GETS PHOTO.	DUBBILEX PRONOUNCES SUPERMAN "DEAD" "HE'S GONE..." EVERYONE AFRAID OF D.D... IS IT DEAD? IF NOT... WE GOTTA KILL IT! / BODIES MOVED. JIMMY GOT BEST PHOTO OF CAREER... "WHY'D IT HAVE TO BE THIS?" ③ LOIS VERY "STRONG" EVERYONE WEARS BLACK S-SHIELD ARMBANDS.	CLARK "MISSING" BUT SO ARE MANY IN DEBRIS OF FIGHT! SUPERGIRL TRIES TO TAKE UP SUPES' POSITION AS HERO OF METROPOLIS... LEX IN CHARGE... "TOO EASY"... LEX HAS SUPER-GIRL BUILD HERO'S TOMB, METROPOLIS TRIES TO RECOVER... BURIED HEROES.

MAN OF STEEL # 20	SUPERMAN # 76, 9PC	ADVENTURES #499	ACTION # 686 9PC
SUPERHERO STUDDED FUNERAL OF SUPES... AND SUPES' BURIAL ⑤ MA + PA NOT AT FUNERAL ..."CAN'T GET BODY"... GRIEF OF OUTLIVING SON! THEY "BURY" CLARK (HIS STUFF) AT SITE OF ROCKET CRASH. MA+PA GO TO BE WITH LOIS... STILL DOING BEST	LOIS, MA + PA GO TO CLARK'S APARTMENT TO PACK UP HIS STUFF. LOIS LOSES IT! ⑥ LANA SHOWS UP... "GRIEF ISSUE!" SET UP WESTFIELD STUFF AS POSSIBLE. SUPES'S BODY IS STOLEN FROM TOMB... FROM UNDERGROUND LOIS, LANA, MA+PA GO TO SUPES TOMB, MA+PA BACK TO SMALLVILLE	① "WHO IS BURIED IN SUPES' TOMB? ⑦ S-GIRL REPLYS CAN'T CUT IT AFTER ALL! SUPES REALLY BEING DEAD-- I GOT AWAY WITH THIS GAG ONCE... ORDERS SUPERGIRL TO CHECK TOMB. IT'S EMPTY. S.C.U. INVESTIGATES POSSIBLE BODY SNATCHERS... TURPIN-- UNDERWORLD AS BODYSNATCHERS"... UW, GUY FIGHTS TURPIN REAFFIRMED AS TOUGHEST COP IN WORLD! UW, PROVES IT AIN'T GOT SUPES' BODY	① "SUPES GETS PARANOID ABOUT BEING DEAD-- LEX REALLY PARANOID S-GIRL AS HERO... OTHR METRO HERO GETTING WORN OUT.

MAN OF STEEL #21	SUPERMAN # 77, 9PC	LEGACY O'SUPERMAN
SUPES'S BODY IS IN CADMUS... AND DUBBILEX SPENDS DAYS WAITING FOR SIGN OF LIFE! ⑨ IN SMALLVILLE PA KENT'S BEEN NEGLECTING FARM DUTIES... MA TELLS HIM LIFE GOES ON... SHE'S BEEN OPTIMISTIC... AN ARGUMENT ENSUES AND PA KENT HAS A HEART ATTACK! PEOPLE CAPITALIZE ON SUPES DEATH... {SUPERMAN IS STILL DEAD!!!!}	"TWO HEART BEATS" ⑩ MXY COMES TO EARTH... BUT SUPERGIRL DOESN'T GET IT... MXY LEAVES..."NOBODY LAUGHS" MANSUL ARRIVES ON EARTH... SITS ON GRAVE, LEAVES... (IN PROGRESS) PA KENT'S HEART IS STOPPING ..."GHOST OF SUPERMAN APPEARS."	5 ELEVEN PAGE STORIES 1- GUARDIAN + N-BOYS 2- ROSE & THORN 3- SINBAD 4- GANGBUSTER 5- LINEAR MEN! DOUBLE-SIZED ISSUE!